PSALMS FOR TODAY

FULL MUSIC EDITION

Edited by
Michael Perry and David Iliff

Jubilate

in association with CPAS

Hodder & Stoughton

LONDON SYDNEY AUCKLAND TORONTO

Also from Jubilate Hymns, published by Hodder and Stoughton:

Hymns for Today's Church
Carols for Today
Church Family Worship
Songs from the Psalms

Copyright Information
Every effort to trace copyright-holders and to obtain permission has been made; the publishers would welcome details of any errors or omissions. Corrections will be incorporated into future reprints. This title is available in the USA from Hope Publishing Company, Carol Stream, Illinois 60188, USA.

British Library Cataloguing in Publication Data

Psalms for Today
  1. Psalms, English
  I. Perry, Michael   II. Iliff, David

ISBN 0 340 50700 4 hbk
    0 340 52826 5 pbk

CONTENTS

CONTENTS

PREFACE

The Psalms are an inheritance of the Christian Church, and its basic hymn book. Many if not most of the hymns we sing – certainly the lasting ones – owe their existence to a psalm. Psalms are the encouragement of our spiritual growth, the reminder of God's omnipotence and ever-presence; they are the celebration of our life in Christ and the consolation of our dying.

How were the Psalms first used? A good proportion of them have notes as to their dedication or origin, and about how they are to be performed. Terms which apparently refer to instruments and tunes are obscure so that, on the whole, their interpretation is conjectural. There is little doubt about 'with stringed instruments' (Psalm 4); but 'for the flutes' is just one possible rendering of a phrase which occurs only in Psalm 5. The sense of the Hebrew 'choral' directions is similarly uncertain. But they do suggest energy, variety, and special use for certain occasions. Most of our evidence for the purpose and early use of psalms comes from the text itself. For instance, there is a huge difference between a psalm of individual confidence or sorrow, and a psalm of communal thanksgiving.

Individual psalms – for instance, the laments – are often packed by the psalmist with human experiences, evidently to meet the pastoral situation of various individuals. Whoever was the contemporary custodian of the psalms at temple or shrine, meeting-place or (later) synagogue, would thus be equipped to articulate the unexpressed needs of the worshipper – not only in public services, but also in private counselling.

In the course of our work on *Psalms for Today* we were tempted to omit some examples as too individualistic, or too specific to translate into anything a congregation would wish to sing. Psalms must say what we want to say to God, or be vehicles of God's word to us – often both; the uncritical recitation of *every* psalm no longer appeals. A closer look assured us that many of the psalms more difficult to render have much to say to a society beset by personal frustrations and anxieties, and can in worship be most expressive of our human condition. We found ways to generalise – '*When* the waters cover me' (69A) – to distil the essence of a psalm, and so to claim it with integrity for congregational use.

At the other end of the scale are the great communal worship songs – many apparently tied to a recurring event or festival. The clearest example is Psalm 118. Here the temple congregation gives thanks, and sings 'God's love is eternal'; the symbolic would-be worshipper stands at the door and asks for entrance. Persons in authority assert: 'This is the gate of the Lord; only the righteous can come in'. God's goodness and salvation is declared by the worshipper. There is a blessing: 'May God bless the one who comes in the name of the Lord'. Then action begins; the master of ceremonies orders: 'With branches in your hands, start the festival and march round the altar'. How did we ever imagine that this psalm might be treated as a straight poem, let alone that it should be chanted – including this stage instruction – in complete ignorance of its intended setting and without distinction of one part from another?

These examples serve to demonstrate the varied texture of the Psalms – a diversity which needs to be reflected in the breadth of treatment given by such a collection for the church as *Psalms for Today*. Here are all manner of psalm versions: some strictly to metre, others responsive, and yet others pointed for chanting or arranged for choral speaking. The music includes popular hymn tunes and other familiar melodies, new tunes and special settings. All are employed to reflect the spirit and enhance the mood of the text. According to the tradition of metrical psalmody we have permitted the 'Christianising' of psalms in some cases – not least when the content has long been appreciated as pointing to the coming Messiah.

As many psalms as could reasonably be offered in a form for worship are represented in *Psalms for Today* – the more versatile psalms by several versions. Always we looked for one version that could be readily used without notice or rehearsal. After that we felt at liberty to extend the range by more adventurous treatment. In this volume we insisted upon competent music and well-crafted text. For occasions where a freer musical style and an informal verbal expression is appropriate, we defer to our companion publication *Songs from the Psalms*. For churches where both hymns and songs are in use there is a combined words edition.

Authors and editors alike must acknowledge the debt to earlier collections of psalm versions – even from the uncharted past – whose extensive influence on the church's music is seen in its liturgies and hymn books. In the early 1970s our first – sometimes heavy-handed – efforts in *Psalm Praise* gave us a taste for the spiritual profundity of our source material in the Hebrew Scriptures, and a love for the words and music of worship. For this we owe special thanks to Michael Baughen, Chairman of Jubilate Hymns and Bishop of Chester, who drew us together on that project, and to the Church Pastoral Aid Society who first published our work. As the years have gone by other writers and musicians have associated themselves with us. We hope that our own standards have improved as we have seen our work in use; and that thereby we have become better practitioners, and not merely theorists. Not one of our humble attempts at paraphrase can match the worth of the Psalms themselves, nor be allowed to displace the translated text in Christian devotion. But we offer them for worship and by way of introduction. All the while, the Psalms, profound, unsurpassable, have been a challenge and an example to our writing. It is something of their profundity and not our own transient views that we have sought to offer in *Psalms for Today*.

We thank most sincerely our Jubilate colleagues, whose help and advice has been unstinting; the wider group of associate writers and musicians whose skills and gifts we have been able to call upon; our energetic publishers; and that inner group of Jubilate staff without whose talent and devotion we would have ceased to function long ago.

MICHAEL PERRY, Tonbridge
DAVID ILIFF, Brussels
Epiphany 1990

USING *PSALMS FOR TODAY*

In the Church of England

The practice of chanting pointed psalms only came into general use in parish churches during the latter part of the nineteenth century. This style is found beautiful and helpful by many, but it has to be acknowledged that more worshippers are defeated by the technicalities of pointing and wish consequently to discontinue the use of psalms.

The move towards Parish Communion as the main Sunday service has reduced the opportunity for psalm and canticle singing. Morning and Evening Prayer (Matins and Evensong) traditionally provided for three or four canticles to be sung, and because these services are used less often, the Psalter has become much less well-known.

The Church of England has in fact lost part of the genius of its heritage. The recital of the psalms at the offices according to a regular pattern dates back to very early times. The Book of Common Prayer Psalter ensures the public reading of every psalm once a month. But quite apart from tradition, the persistent omission of the Psalms deprives the Church of a pillar of its spirituality. As a consequence the Church is unable to offer the resources of the Psalms, which so squarely face up to the human condition, as it tries to meet the needs of the present secular generation. Where is the remedy?

The Anglican congregation today has much more influence in what it says and sings in church. Through the Parochial Church Council, changes of direction in worship have to be agreed with the incumbent, with the bishop as final arbiter. The incumbent, who has theological training and professional liturgical and pastoral advice to offer, will be allowed to lead if the PCC is wise; and the incumbent will keep the musician in his confidence if he has sense and foresight. An awareness by the minister, musician and church council of the gradual demise of the Psalms is important. *Psalms for Today* may be used to remedy this situation. How can it best be used?

We suggest that the choice of psalms from *Psalms for Today* follows the promptings of the Lectionary, or matches the minister's or preacher's chosen theme. The Themes Index, the Liturgical Index and the Lectionary Index will help with subjects and seasons.

Experienced practitioners will know that it is unwise to introduce too many new tunes at once – especially where there is neither choir nor active tradition of congregational singing. Most of the metrical versions in *Psalms for Today* are cross-referenced to known hymn tunes, and may be used this way while the book is being introduced. There is, however, a danger here: the peril of monotony if every psalm version is set to a known hymn tune. With choices from the hymn book already made, Morning or Evening Prayer (Matins or Evensong) could end up in effect with seven hymns! The Psalms need to contrast with the hymns on such an occasion. The 'known' hymn tunes here set or recommended should therefore be used for psalms with economy and good judgement.

To provide a different style of music from the traditional hymn, extensive use has been made of folk-song tunes, early nineteenth century American tunes, responsive tunes, and tunes newly-composed. Chants for pointed versions of well-known psalms and canticles are also provided. They are printed without definite note values in order to encourage singing in rhythms dictated by natural speech rather than those imposed by a beat. A choir practising chanted psalms and canticles is recommended to *say* the words through, at a deliberate pace, before singing them. This will make clear where natural emphases should come and these should be incorporated as far as possible in the sung performance.

With such variety there is considerable scope for balanced choice in a service where more than one psalm/canticle is needed.

Some churches will wish to use this Psalm book exclusively. Others, especially where the song genre is popular, may prefer to use our companion volume *Songs from the Psalms* in conjunction. The words edition is a combined one, and includes songs based on psalms as well as the texts set here in *Psalms for Today*. This means there need be only one financial outlay involved in equipping the congregation. The two music books have been kept separate, to keep costs lower and because the musical styles are different. Using both music books (one words book) gives even greater flexibility in choice and balance.

In the Free Churches

Today's Free Churches, whose forebears developed metrical psalmody, received from them a host of psalm texts. But they did not feel the obligation to use them systematically, as Anglicans used the psalter. In the eighteenth century, the flowering of hymnody in the Free Churches tended to eclipse the metrical psalms – although Spurgeon's *Our Own Hymn-book* (1866) devoted its first 150 numbers to a complete metrical psalter, and *Wesley's Hymns* (1889) still had a large selection of metrical psalms. Many of the traditional texts are rigidly long metre or common metre, and this gives them a bland, even monotonous, feel. Their dated appeal, and the absence of any system of psalm use in the less structured worship of the Free Churches led to their gradual demise.

The losers are the congregation, because they no longer have that close acquaintance with the spirituality of the Psalms which is the inheritance of all Christendom. *Psalms for Today* presents churches and congregations with an opportunity to put the matter right. Published and recognised hymn-writers of the leading denominations have united to craft new psalm versions. The work spans twenty years. We hope that congregations which have embraced new hymns and Christian songs will warm to these texts which combine a fresh approach with biblical statements of faith, worship and aspiration.

Psalms may be chosen to match the movement of worship in the Free Churches: Approach to Worship/Thanksgiving; Scripture Reading and Teaching; Prayer and Intercession; Praise; Proclamation, Challenge and Dedication. The thematic index will offer the minister or group leader a considerable resource for combining worship with teaching.

More recently there has been a call in Free Church circles for spoken material suitable for use by minister and congregation – something almost unheard of even ten years ago. Words are wanted which involve the people and demonstrate that verbal worship is not just the province of the minister. But for the Free Churches, to return to the slavish commitment to repetition of traditional texts (and archaism) that has been the diet of the established church until now simply would not do. A contemporary and much more participatory diet is required. We believe that the *Psalms for Today* appendix of forty spoken psalm versions goes some way towards meeting that demand.

Our hope is that *Psalms for Today* will be warmly received in the Free Churches, not only because it can enable greater congregational participation, but also because it makes accessible the incomparable spirituality of the Psalms.

In the Roman Catholic Church

Until the Second Vatican Council, the Roman Catholic Church used almost exclusively Gregorian psalm-tones, with antiphons before and after each psalm. This world-wide practice employed the Latin text whenever a monastic or neo-monastic office was sung. The exception was the Gelineau form of vernacular psalmody which is now little used;

although it is more prevalent in the United States than in the United Kingdom. At Mass, a psalm-verse or two would be sung during the Gradual or Alleluia between the readings (again with a Latin text), using either very florid plainchant or, less often, polyphonic or fauxbourdon settings. These chants were reserved for the choir.

Since Vatican II, the Sunday and Weekday Lectionary has contained a responsive psalm after the first reading at Mass. A congregational response occurs every four or six lines; the normal practice is for the congregation to sing the refrain, and for a cantor – or a group of cantors – to sing the verses. A substantial majority of the psalm-tones used are of the 'reciting note with termination' type. There is now an increasing use of psalm *tunes* (tones in regular metres).

As regards translation, the Grail version is almost universal for the English-speaking world (the USA also uses NAB). Specific examples of the Gelineau form (for which the Grail text was designed) still appeal, though the generality does not. Probably it was ahead of its time, becoming available before the use of the vernacular at Mass. By the time that departure was authorised, taste and opinion had moved on; the text, however, has remained.

Less than half of English-speaking Catholic congregations sing any psalm at all, the responsive psalm being said. And, although various styles of psalm are attempted by forward-looking Catholics, these are often employed for exits, entrances, communion etc. and do not occupy the traditional positions in the service.

For monastic, or neo-monastic, offices today, most communities sing the psalms in English, using similar tones to those mentioned above; some communities still preserve some Latin psalmody to Gregorian tones mixed in with vernacular psalmody (though not normally within the same office).

It is remarkable, then, that each tradition – Roman Catholic, Free Church, and Anglican – has lost a significant element of the 'word' service developed by the early Church from their Hebrew inheritance. There are riches to be rediscovered!

Practical Points

None of the performance directions given with the psalm versions are intended to be prescriptive. Indications of speed, or of division of verses between men and women, for example, should be adapted to suit particular local circumstances.

● **Metrical Settings**

Many of these are in four-part harmony but it is suggested that when new tunes are introduced they are sung initially in unison. When descants are used all other voices should sing the melody in unison.

● **Pointed Settings to Chants**

(a) The rhythm and speed of chanting should be that of clear, deliberate speech. Notes in the chants are purposely printed without indication of value in beats.
(b) Normally a breath should be taken at the end of each line. Occasionally an asterisk or double space between words indicates a break.
(c) A dot indicates the division of syllables in a bar when there are more than two syllables.
(d) *Second part* indicates that the music should be begun half-way through the chant.
(e) If it is wished to say rather than sing the psalm the use of bold type indicates how the words may be divided between two groups or between leader and congregation.

● **Responsorial Settings**

Settings such as 42B, 47B, 117B are not necessarily intended for choir alone. The choir may sing the verse sections with the congregation joining in the repeated refrains.

PSALMS, CANTICLES
AND LITURGICAL HYMNS

If we love the word of God

Fullness 7 6 7 6

Words: from Psalm 1
Michael Perry
Music: Noël Tredinnick

UNISON

1 If we love the word of God and____
2 If we shun the sin - ners' way and____
3 If we do these things we'll find rich____

heed it day__ and__ night; if we make God's truth our
spurn their false__ ad - vice; if we turn from God - less
bless - ings as__ we__ go; then we'll flour - ish like a

vv 1 and 2   v 3

law, God's coun-sel our de - light:
lies and e - vils that en - tice:
tree where liv - ing wa - ters   flow.

Alternative tune: Dartmeet, *Songs from the Psalms* 1A

1B(i)   The Law of God

Bibury   8 8 8 8 (LM)

Words: from Psalm 1
Brian Foley
Music: David Iliff

1 The Law of God__ is life to choose, the Will of__ God is joy to__ see, the Word of God is truth__ to speak, the__ Love__ of God__ brings love__ to be!

2 The Law of God__ is no mere list of things to__ do and not to__ do, but God's per-fect-ion— this__ a-lone__ the__ yes__ and no__ of all__ we do!

WOMEN 3 The Will of God__ must be our will, to wish, to__ want, to do, to__ be; and with the mind of God,__ to think, and__ through the eyes__ of God,__ to see!

MEN
4 The Word of God, the voice of God,
was through his Servant-Prophets heard,
in time, foretelling One-to-Come —
his Servant-Son, his living Word!

ALL
5 The Love of God is God himself —
most precious gift that he can give! —
to be in us the cause of love,
to fill with love the life we live!

6 Then make the Law of God our law,
the Will of God our chosen ways,
the Word of God our firmest faith,
and God himself our endless praise!

The Law of God

Melcombe 8 8 8 8 (LM)

Words: from Psalm 1
Brian Foley
Music: S Webbe the elder (1740–1816)

1 The Law of___ God is___ life to choose, the
2 The Law of___ God is___ no mere list of
WOMEN 3 The Will of___ God must___ be our will, to

Will of___ God is joy to___ see, the Word of___ God is
things to___ do and not to___ do, but God's per - fect - ion –
wish, to___ want, to do, to___ be; and with the___ mind of

truth to speak, the Love of___ God brings love to___ be!
this a - lone the yes and___ no of all we___ do!
God, to think, and through the___ eyes of God, to___ see!

MEN

4 The Word of God, the voice of God,
   was through his Servant-Prophets heard,
   in time, foretelling One-to-Come –
   his Servant-Son, his living Word!

ALL

5 The Love of God is God himself –
   most precious gift that he can give! –
   to be in us the cause of love,
   to fill with love the life we live!

6 Then make the Law of God our law,
   the Will of God our chosen ways,
   the Word of God our firmest faith,
   and God himself our endless praise!

1C Blessed are they

Coln Rogers 39363785

Words: from Psalm 1
Paul Wigmore
Music: John Barnard

UNISON

1 Blessed are they who lis-ten not to e-vil coun-sel,
2 Blessed are they, for as a tree by streams of wa-ter
3 Blessed are they though sin-ners like the chaff be scat-tered,

turn a-side from ev-ery thought of sin:
spreads its leaves in boun-ti-ful dis-plays,
blessed are they though winds of judge-ment blow;

day and night, the law of God their mak-er
bears and yields its rip-ened fruit in sea-son—
from the Lord, up-on his right-eous ser-vants,

is their joy and me-di-ta-tion, well of life with-in.
so shall they in ev-ery call-ing pros-per all their days.
lov-ing care and ten-der mer-cies ev-er-more shall flow.

4

How many are against me, Lord

3A

Solothurn 8 8 8 8 (LM)

Words: from Psalm 3
Christopher Idle
Music: Swiss traditional melody
arranged C H Kitson (1874–1944)

1 How ma - ny are a - gainst me, Lord: how
2 But you are round me, Lord, my shield; but
3 I go to rest, and sleep in peace — I

ma - ny fierce at - tacks rise up! They say 'God will not
you, my glo - ry, lift my head! You hear me from your
wake a - gain; God keeps me safe: ten thou - sand shall not

come to help' and peo - ple taunt, 'There is no hope.'
ho - ly hill and ans - wer when I cry a - loud.
make me fear, for all their threats to take my life.

4 Arise, O Lord, to rescue me:
arise and save me, O my God!
You silence all my enemies
till scorn and spite are all destroyed.

5 Your blessings, Father, grant to us;
your help, O Saviour, still be ours:
O Holy Spirit, fill our lives –
to God be glory, love, and praise!

O God, defender of the poor

Liverpool 8 6 8 6 (CM)

Words: from Psalm 4
Christopher Idle
Music: American folk melody
arranged John Barnard

1 O God, de - fen - der of the poor, have
2 How long will peo - ple choose vain things, love
3 The saints, O Lord, you set a - part by

mer - cy when I pray: you lis - tened to my
emp - ty words and wrong? They scorn to serve the
grace to be your own: let sin - ners trem - ble,

prayer be - fore Lord, hear my prayer to - day!
King of kings O liv - ing God, how long?
search their hearts, and bow be - fore your throne.

WOMEN

4 While many pray that you will bless
and bring them all they need,
unless they long for holiness
their prayers are vain indeed.

MEN

5 Your light, O Lord, let us receive,
your face within us shine:
for richer is the joy you give
than all their corn and wine.

ALL

6 And even when I turn to sleep
your blessings still increase,
for you alone, O Lord, will keep
your child in perfect peace.

Alternative tune: Abridge, *Hymns for Today's Church* 374

Lord, as I wake

Bolnhurst 8 8 8 8 (LM)

Words: from Psalm 5
Brian Foley
Music: Paul Edwards

1 Lord, as I wake I turn to you, your -
2 There is no bless - ing, Lord, from you for_____
3 Your lov - ing gifts of grace to me, those_____
4 Lord, make my life a life of love, keep_____

- self the first thought of my day;_____ my king, my God, whose help is
those who make their will their way,_____ no praise for those who will not
fa - vours I could ne - ver earn,_____ call for my thanks in praise and
me from sin in all I do;_____ Lord, make your law my on - ly

sure,_____ your - self the help_____ for which I pray.
praise,_____ no peace for those_____ who will not pray.
prayer,_____ call me to love_____ you in re - turn.
law,_____ your will my will,_____ for love of you.

Words: from the *New Catholic Hymnal*
© 1971 Faber Music Ltd, 3 Queen Square,
London WC1N 3AU

5(ii)

Lord, as I wake

Daniel 8 8 8 8 (LM)

Words: from Psalm 5
Brian Foley
Music: Irish traditional melody
arranged David Iliff

1 Lord, as I wake I turn to you, your-
2 There is no bless-ing, Lord, from you for
3 Your lov-ing gifts of grace to me, those
4 Lord, make my life a life of love, keep

-self the first thought of my day; my king, my God, whose
those who make their will their way, no praise for those who
fa-vours I could ne-ver earn, call for my thanks in
me from sin in all I do; Lord, make your law my

help is sure, your-self the help for which I pray.
will not praise, no peace for those who will not pray.
praise and prayer, call me to love you in re-turn.
on-ly law, your will my will, for love of you.

Words: from the *New Catholic Hymnal*
© 1971 Faber Music Ltd, 3 Queen Square,
London WC1N 3AU

8

O gracious Lord

6

St Alphege 7 6 7 6

Words: from Psalm 6
Michael Perry
Music: H J Gauntlett (1805–1876)

1 O gra - cious Lord, be near me! My
2 'How shall the voice you gave me sing
3 I knew the fear of dy - ing, and

soul cries out, 'How long? When will you turn to
prais - es from the dead? Re - turn, O Lord, and
sor - row filled my eyes; but God who hears my

hear_____ me and save your child from wrong?'
save_____ me; in love lift up my head.'
cry - ing, in judge - ment will a - rise!

Alternative tune: Kocher, *Hymns for Today's Church* 530

7A · I will give thanks

Hiding-place

Words: from Psalm 7
Michael Perry
Music: David Iliff

Refrain UNISON

I will give thanks to the Lord most high;— I will sing praise to his right-eous name.

Fine

Verse

1 I have no strength but___ yours,___ O
2 To love that will not___ cease___ I
3 My God, my sove - reign___ still,___ my

God, my hid - ing - place; you snatch me from the
owe my life, my___ all;___ and just - ly if I
shield, my joy, my___ crown: you hon - our those who

This Psalm version can be sung without the refrain to Venice,
Psalms for Today 133A(ii), *Hymns for Today's Church* 34.

li - on's claws and save me by your grace.
break God's peace then pun - ish - ment will fall.
do your will, you tread the e - vil down.

OPTIONAL HARMONY for Verse 2

2 To love that will not cease I
   will not cease

owe my life, my all; and just - ly if I
    life, my all;

break God's peace then pun - ish - ment will fall.
break God's peace then pun - ish - ment will fall.

The Harmony and Unison versions are harmonically compatible.

8A(i)   Lord, how majestic is your name

Jacob's Well   8 7 8 7

Words: from Psalm 8
Fred Kaan
Music: Barry Rose

1 Lord, how ma - jes - tic is your name! The
2 When I look up and see the stars and
3 You lift us to the ve - ry height of

earth and sky a - dore you, the mouths of ba - bies
think of space un - end - ing, I mar - vel that you
your cre - a - tive like - ness, just as you raised your

sing your praise and child - ren dance be - fore you.
come and care, us with your love be - friend - ing.
Son from death to Eas - ter's wide - a - wake - ness.

Words: © Stainer & Bell Ltd,
82 High Road, London N2 9PW

Lord, how majestic is your name

8A(ii)

Ach, Gott und Herr 8 7 8 7

Words: from Psalm 8
Fred Kaan
Music: *Neu Leipziger Gesangbuch* 1682
arranged J S Bach (1685–1750)

1 Lord, how ma - jes - tic___ is___ your name! The
2 When I look up and___ see___ the stars and
3 You lift us to the___ ve - ry height of

earth _and_ sky a - dore___ you, the mouths of ba - bies
think _of_ space un - end - ing, I mar - vel that you
your _cre - a - tive_ like - ness, just as you raised your

sing__ your_ praise and child - ren dance be - fore___ you.
come_ and_ care, us with your love__ be - friend - ing.
Son__ from_ death to Eas - ter's wide - a - wake - ness.

8B(i)

With wonder, Lord

Manton Hollow 8 8 8 4

Words: from Psalm 8
Brian Foley
Music: John Barnard

UNISON

1	With	won - der, Lord, we	see	your	works,_____	we
(2	With)	won - der, Lord, we	see	your	works,_____	and
(3	The)	stars that fill the	skies	a -	bove,_____	the
(4	We)	praise your works, yet we	our -	selves_____	are
(5	All)	you have made is	ours	to	rule,_____	the

see the beau - ty you have	made;_____	this	earth, the skies, all things that
child-like in our joy we	sing_____	to	praise you, bless you, mak - er,
sun and moon which give our	light,_____	are	your de - sign - ing for our
works of won - der made by	you;_____	not	far from you in all we
birds and beasts at will to	tame,_____	all	things to or - der for the

vv 1-4   v 5

are	in beau-ty made.	2 With
Lord	of ev - ery-thing.	3 The	glo - ry of your name.
use	and our de-light.	4 We
are	and all we do.	5 All

Music: © John Barnard/Jubilate Hymns †

Words: © 1971 Faber Music Ltd,
3 Queen Square, London WC1N 3AU

14

With wonder, Lord

Es ist kein Tag 8 8 8 4

Words: from Psalm 8
Brian Foley
Music: J D Meyer (1692)

1 With won - der, Lord, we see your works, we
2 With won - der, Lord, we see your works, and
3 The stars that fill the skies a - bove, the
4 We praise your works, yet we our - selves are
5 All you have made is ours to rule, the

see the beau - ty you have made; this earth, the skies, all
child - like in our joy we sing to praise you, bless you,
sun and moon which give our light, are your de - sign - ing
works of won - der made by you; not far from you in
birds and beasts at will to tame, all things to or - der

things that are in beau - ty made.
mak - er, Lord of ev - ery - thing.
for our use and our de - light.
all we are and all we do.
for the glo - ry of your name.

Alternative tune: Almsgiving, *Hymns for Today's Church* 287

Words: © 1971 Faber Music Ltd,
3 Queen Square, London WC1N 3AU

O Lord our Governor

Words: Psalm 8
from *The Liturgical Psalter*
David Frost and others
Music: G M Garrett (1834–1897)
Descant: John Barnard

1 O ˈ Lord our ˈ Governor:
   how glorious is your ˈ name in ˈ all the ˈ earth!
2 Your majesty above the heavens is ˈ yet reˈcounted:
   by the ˈ mouths of ˈ babes and ˈ sucklings.

Second part
3 You have founded a strong defence aˈgainst your ˈ adversaries:
   to quell the ˈ ene·my ˈ and · the aˈvenger.

4 When I consider your heavens the ˈ work of · your ˈ fingers:
   the moon and the stars which ˈ you have ˈ set in ˈ order,
5 what is man   that you should be ˈ mindful ˈ of him:
   or the son of ˈ man that ˈ you should ˈ care for him?

6 Yet you have made him little ˈ less · than a ˈ god:
   and have ˈ crowned him · with ˈ glory · and ˈ honour.
7 You have made him the ˈ master · of your ˈ handiwork:
   and have put all things in subˈjection · beˈneath his ˈ feet,

8 all ˈ sheep and ˈ oxen:
   and all the ˈ creatures ˈ of the ˈ field,
9 the birds of the air and the ˈ fish · of the ˈ sea:
   and everything that moves in the pathways ˈ of the ˈ great ˈ waters.

Second part
10 O ˈ Lord our ˈ Governor:
    how glorious is your ˈ name in ˈ all the ˈ earth!

    Glory to the Father and ˈ to the ˈ Son:
    and ˈ to the ˈ Holy ˈ Spirit;
    as it was in the beˈginning · is ˈ now:
    and shall be for ˈ ever. ˈ Aˈmen.

I praise you, Lord

Confitebor tibi

Words: from Psalm 9
Michael Perry
Music: David Llewellyn Green

Alternative tune: *Songs from the Psalms 9*

Music: © David Llewellyn Green

Words: © Michael Perry/Jubilate Hymns †

10(i) In my hour of grief or need

Lewknor 7 7 7 7

Words: from Psalm 10
Timothy Dudley-Smith
Music: John Barnard

DESCANT

6 Then shall vice and false-hood fail, truth and right-eous -

UNISON

1 In my hour of grief or need when a friend is
2 When the powers of e - vil ride through the world in
6 Then shall vice and false-hood fail, truth and right-eous -

- ness pre - vail, all his ran - somed

friend in - deed, now, when Sa - tan
o - pen pride, flaunt - ed sins and
- ness pre - vail, all his ran - somed

peo - ple sing___ God, their ev - er - last - ing King!

walks a-broad, be not far from me, O Lord.
boast - ed shame bring con-tempt up - on your name –
peo - ple sing God, their ev - er - last - ing King!

v 6

3 When the god-less man is strong;— when his mouth is
4 When the poor be-comes his prey,— when the weak are
5 Powers of dark-ness bring to grief, break the hold of

filled with wrong,— bit - ter - ness, de -
led a - stray,— right is wrong and
un - be - lief,— sound a - new the

- ceit and fraud,— be not far from me, O Lord.
truth is lies = then, O Lord our God, a - rise!
quick - ening word = rise and come a - mong us, Lord!

D.C. for verse 6

The Unison and Harmony versions are harmonically compatible.
The Unison version should be used for the accompaniment throughout.

19

10(ii)   In my hour of grief or need

Heinlein   7 7 7 7

Words: from Psalm 10
Timothy Dudley-Smith
Music: *Nürnbergisches Gesangbuch* 1676
attributed to M Herbst (1654–1681)

1 In my hour of grief or need when a friend is
2 When the powers of evil ride through the world in
3 When the godless man is strong; when his mouth is

friend in deed, now, when Satan
o pen pride, flaunt ed sins and
filled with wrong, bit ter ness, de -

walks a-broad, be not far from me, O Lord.
boast ed shame bring con tempt up on your name –
-ceit and fraud, be not far from me, O Lord.

4 When the poor becomes his prey,
   when the weak are led astray,
   right is wrong and truth is lies –
   then, O Lord our God, arise!

5 Powers of darkness bring to grief,
   break the hold of unbelief,
   sound anew the quickening word –
   rise and come among us, Lord!

6 Then shall vice and falsehood fail,
   truth and righteousness prevail,
   all his ransomed people sing
   God, their everlasting King!

I find my refuge in the Lord

Everberg 8 8 8 8 (LM)

Words: from Psalm 11
Basil Bridge
Music: David Iliff

UNISON

1 I find my re - fuge in the Lord, no
2 The Lord is in his ho - ly place, en -
3 He knows what I through shame con - ceal, yet

fears shall make me fly a - way: the moun - tains hide the hunt - ed
- throned on high, yet near at hand; both saint and sin - ner come to
of - fers me this cup of grace: his Spi - rit's fire will cleanse and

bird; his truth stands firm — with him I stay.
face his judge - ment, in his pres - ence stand.
heal, the up - right shall be - hold his face.

Alternative tunes: Bow Brickhill or Breslau, *Hymns for Today's Church* 146

12A

God will arise

Salvum me fac

Words: from Psalm 12
Michael Perry
Music: Anthony Greening

Con moto

Refrain
UNISON

God will a -

Man.

-rise be - cause the weak are __ cry - ing,

Ped.

God will a - rise be - cause the need - y __ call,

God will a-rise who_ knows and_ loves them all.

Verses

1 Flaw - less are God's migh - ty words – sil - ver forged in__ fire,_____
2 When the wick - ed strut a - bout, when they take the_ sword,_____

mf

D.C.

sham - ing ev - ery_ e - vil tongue, ev - ery dark de - sire._____
hear your peo - ple_ in their pain, come to us, O__ Lord!_____

Optional Harmony version for Refrain overleaf

OPTIONAL HARMONY for Refrain

God will a - rise_____ be -

God will a - rise be -

- cause the weak are_____ cry - ing, God will a -

- cause the weak are cry - ing,

- rise_____ be - cause the need - y_____ call,_____

God will a - rise be - cause the need - y call,_____

God will a - rise_____ who_ knows and_ loves them all._____

God will a - rise He loves them all._____

The accompaniment on pages 22 and 23 should be used with this version.

The promises of God

Bramdean 8 8 8 7

Words: from Psalm 12
Keith Landis
Music: Barry Rose

1 The pro - mis - es of God are pure, as
2 The pro - mis - es of God re - mind my
3 The pro - mis - es of God are right, as

tem - pered steel made keen and sure, by ham - mer - blows forged
soul of sil - ver well - re - fined, a match - less cup by
fin - est gold, most pre - cious, bright, su - perb - ly wrought for

vv 1 and 2   **v 3**

to en - dure, a sword for my de - fend - ing.
Love de-signed, di - vine e - lix - ir blend - ing.
my de - light, a crown of life un - - end - ing.

13A How long will you forget me, Lord

Bangor 8 6 8 6 (CM)

Words: from Psalm 13
Christopher Idle
Music: from W Tans'ur's *Harmony of Syon* 1734

1 How long will you_ for - get me,_ Lord, and
2 Look on my need,_ O Lord my_ God who
3 Look on their threats_ and hear my_ cry, and
4 But since I trust_ your con - stant_ love my

hide_ your_ face a - way? How_ long shall e - vils_
grants my_ ev - ery breath; give_ light that I may_
ans - wer when I call: or_ they will claim the_
heart_ is_ glad and free to_ sing the prais - es_

tear_ my heart and_ trou - bles fill my day?
see_ your light, not_ sleep the_ sleep of death.
vic - to - ry who_ long to_ see me fall.
of_ the_ Lord for_ all your_ grace to me.

The fool whose heart declares in pride

Detroit 8 6 8 6 (CM)

Words: from Psalm 14
Stephen Wilcockson
Music: *Supplement to the Kentucky Harmony* 1820
arranged David Iliff

1 The fool whose heart de - clares_ in_ pride, 'There
2 For all have sinned and turned_ from_ God, not_
3 Do they not know, can they not_ tell, who_
4 Now come, O Lord, your peo - ple_ bless, and

is no God to_ fear,' for - gets_ the_ Lord's all -
one has kept God's way; cor - rupt_ a - like,_ not
plan to_ crush the_ poor, that_ God is_ with_ the
pu - ri - fy from_ wrong, that_ we_ may make_ your

- see - ing_ eye who finds no good - ness_ here:
one_ does_ good – we all have gone_ a - stray.
right - eous_ still, their re - fuge ev - er_ sure?
right - eous - ness our ev - er - last - ing_ song!

Alternative tune: Stracathro, *Psalms for Today* 165B(ii), *Hymns for Today's Church* 144

Music arrangement: © David Iliff/Jubilate Hymns †   Words: © Stephen Wilcockson

15A   Lord, who may dwell within your house

Withington 868886

Words: from Psalm 15
Paul Wigmore
Music: John Barnard

1 Lord, who may dwell with-in your house and on_ your ho-ly
2 All those who love their neigh-bour well, who hate_ the way of

hill? All those who walk a blame-less way, who
sin, who hon-our all that fear the Lord, whose

love the right, who win the day with truth-ful words and,
pro-mise is a bind-ing cord, who help, and seek no

come what may, will speak no word of ill:
rich re-ward – these, Lord, you wel-come in.

Lord, who may venture where you dwell   15B

Wells House   8 8 8 8 (LM)

Words: from Psalm 15
David Preston
Music: David Iliff

UNISON

1 Lord, who may ven-ture where you dwell,   or   wor-ship on your ho-ly   hill?   The
2 They ne-ver do their neigh-bour wrong,   and   ut-ter no ma-li-cious word;   the
3 They keep their oath at   a-ny   cost,   and   glad-ly lend, but not for   gain;   they

pure in heart, whose spot-less lives   by   word and deed o-bey your will.
sin-ner's fol-ly they des-pise,   but   hon-our those who fear the Lord.
hate all bribe-ry: come what may,   se-cure for ev-er they re-main.

Alternative tune: Breslau, *Hymns for Today's Church* 146

16A
I set the Lord before my eyes

Palace Green 8 7 8 7 8 8 7

Words: from Psalm 16
Owen Dowling
Music: Michael Fleming

1 I___ set the Lord be-fore my eyes,___ and look in long-ing to___ him;
2 The___ One who takes the fear from death___ turns dark-ness in - to dawn-ing;

Christ calls me dai - ly to a - rise___ from fear and an - xious striv - ing.
my___ spi - rit and my mind give birth___ to prais - es fresh each morn - ing.

At___ my right hand he al - ways moves, the path through dark - ened plac - es shows,
All___ night - ly fears will now de - part, for hope se - cure with - in the heart

UNISON

his hold is firm, con - sol - ing.
is found with Christ's ap - pear - ing.

Alternative tune: Luther, *Psalms for Today* 29A, *Hymns for Today's Church* 189

Lord of all my footsteps

Cogenhoe 6 5 6 5

Words: from Psalm 17
David Mowbray
Music: Paul Edwards

UNISON

1 Lord of all my foot - steps, watch - ing from a - bove,
2 O - thers moved by ma - lice spread un - truths a - round:
3 For their hope is rich - es, time will yet des - troy;

keep me in the safe - ty of your per - fect love.
shall their schemes not fal - ter and their plans re - bound?
you are all my trea - sure and my last - ing joy.

Alternative tune: Caswall, *Hymns for Today's Church* 126

18A

I love you, O Lord

Jane 8 8 8 8 D

Words: from Psalm 18
Christopher Idle
Music: David Peacock

UNISON

1 I love you, O Lord, you a - lone, my___
2 The dan - gers of death gath - ered round, the___
3 The earth and the e - le - ments shake with___
4 My hope is the pro - mise he gives, my___

re - fuge on whom I de - pend; my ma - ker, my sav - iour, my
waves of des - truc - tion came near; but in my des - pair - ing I
thun - der and light - ning and hail; the cliffs and the moun - tain-tops
life is se - cure in his hand; I shall not be lost, for he

own,___ my hope and my trust with-out end._____ The
found___ the Lord who re-leased me from fear._____ I
break___ and mor - tals are fee - ble and pale._____ His
lives!___ He comes to my aid – I shall stand!_____ Lord

Alternative tune: Trewen, *Hymns for Today's Church* 449

Lord is my strength and my song,_____ de-
called for his help in my pain,_____ to
jus - tice is full and com - plete,_____ his
God, you are power - ful to save,_____ your

- fen - der and guide of my ways; my mas - ter to whom I be -
God my sal - va - tion I cried; he brought me his com - fort a -
mer - cy to us has no end; the clouds are a path for his
Spi - rit will spur me to pray; your Son has de - feat - ed the

- long, my God who shall have all my praise.
- gain, I live by the strength he sup - plied.
feet, he comes on the wings of the wind.
grave: I trust and I praise you to - day!

18B(i)   I love you, Lord

Northwood   8 8 8 8 (LM)

Words: from Psalm 18
Keith Landis
Music: David Iliff

UNISON

1 I love you, Lord, my strength and rock, my
2 My God, my ref - uge and my shield, my

health and vig - our, heart-beat, breath, my for - tress
strong - hold and sal - va - tion's door; Lord Christ, most

and de - liv - er - er from death of life and life of death!
wor-thy to be praised, all these you are, yet more – much more!

I love you, Lord

Church Triumphant 8 8 8 8 (LM)

Words: from Psalm 18
Keith Landis
Music: J W Elliott (1833–1915)

1 I love you, Lord, my strength and rock, my___
2 My God, my re - fuge and my shield, my___

health and___ vi - gour, heart - beat, breath, my for - tress and de -
strong - hold___ and sal - va - tion's door; Lord Christ, most wor - thy

-liv - er - er from death of life and life of death!
to be praised, all these you are, yet more – much more!

19A   We look into your heavens

The Linden Tree   8 7 8 7

Words: from Psalm 19
Fred Pratt Green
Music: Old German melody
arranged John Barnard

1 We look in - to your heavens and see your glo - ry
2 We look in - to our way - ward hearts: how wise - ly
3 From mer - cy what have I to hide? You hold me
4 That you ap - prove my spo - ken word, my thoughts and

in cre - a - tion — there's not a sun or
you di - rect us! Your law is where our
back from sin - ning. O let me not be
my be - hav - iour, will be your ser - vant's

ga - lax - y but speaks our a - dor - a - tion.
jus - tice starts, its clear com - mands pro - tect us.
ruled by pride, where sin has its be - gin - ning.
great re - ward, my Sun, my Shield, my Sav - iour!

Alternative tune: St Columba, *Hymns for Today's Church* 404

Music arrangement: © John Barnard/Jubilate Hymns †

Words: © Stainer & Bell Ltd,
82 High Road, London N2 9PW

Glory and praise to God

Water-End

Words: from Psalm 19
Christopher Idle
Music: Geoffrey Shaw (1879–1943)

1 Glo - ry and praise to God! All the skies sing praise –
2 Glo - ry and praise to God for his per - fect law,

songs from the sun and moon, from the nights and days: No hu-man voice is
mak - ing the sim - ple wise and the wav-erer sure. Sweet-er than hon-ey -

there, no mor-tal speech is heard; still through the depths of space speeds the
- comb, rich-er than pur-est gold; praise for re-demp-tion's plan which the

sound - ing word. Up comes the morn - ing sun for his migh - ty
words un - fold. Lord, keep my heart from sin – you have set me

race, and the Lord shines on us with his truth___ and grace.
free: be my life and my light; Je-sus, shine___ on me.

19C — God's glory fills the heavens

St Patrick 8 8 8 8 D

Words: from Psalm 19
Carl P Daw Jnr
Music: Irish traditional hymn melody
arranged C V Stanford (1852–1924)

UNISON

1 God's glo - ry fills___ the heavens with hymns, the domed sky
2 God's per - fect law___ re - vives___ the___ soul,___ its pre - cepts
3 God's ser - vant may___ I ev - er___ be -___ this world my

bears___ the Ma - ker's mark; new prais - es___ sound___ from
make___ the sim - ple wise, its just___ com - mands re -
joy,___ that word my guide: O cleanse___ me,___ Lord,___ from

day to day___ and___ e - cho___ through the know - ing dark. With -
- joice the heart, its___ truth gives light___ un - to the eyes. For
se - cret sin;___ de - li - ver___ me___ from sel - fish pride. Ac -

-out a word their songs roll on — in-to all lands their
ev - er shall this_ law en - dure — un-blem - ished, right-eous,
-cept my thoughts and_ words and deeds; let them find fav - our

voic - es run; and with___ a___ champ - ion's strength and
true, com - plete; no gold___ was_ ev - er found so
in your sight — for you___ a - lone___ can make me

grace__ from_ farth - est__ heaven comes forth the sun.
fine,__ no ho - ney_ in the comb more sweet.
whole,__ O__ Lord my__ re - fuge and my might.

20A May the Lord God hear you pray

Queen's Terrace 7 7 7 7

Words: from Psalm 20
Michael Perry
Music: Norman Warren

1 May the Lord God hear you pray, may God's strength be
2 May God give you all you need, may God make your
3 Now we see the Lord can save, now the trem-bling

yours to - day; may God bless you from a - bove,
plans suc - ceed; may God guide you all your days,
heart is brave; now we know that Love will hear:

vv 1 and 2

lift - ing up your heart in love.
fill - ing all our hearts with praise:

v 3

wor - ship now, for God is near!

Alternative tune: Song 13, *Hymns for Today's Church* 235

With all your heart rejoice

St Austin 8 6 8 6 (CM)

Words: from Psalm 21
David Mowbray
Music: English traditional melody
arranged David Iliff

1 With all your heart re - joice, and sing to
2 A hap - py king who trusts in God, his
3 Yet who, ex - cept the Lord most high, may
4 The King of kings, the Christ of God, to

God the Lord of all! His mer - cy, like a
shin - ing crown se - cure! His face is bright, his
bear the e - ter - nal name, or reign in un - spoilt
whom all power is given! Rise, then, with spi - rit

moun - tain spring, brings life to great and small.
prayers are heard, his throne shall long en - dure.
ma - jes - ty a - bove our world - ly shame?
un - de - terred, and join the praise of heaven!

Alternative tune: St Fulbert, *Hymns for Today's Church* 168

22A(i)   Why, God, have you forsaken me

Attercliffe   8 8 8 8 (LM)

Words: from Psalm 22
Brian Foley
Music: Derek Williams

UNISON

1 Why, God, have you for-sak-en me — more dis-tant now the more I cry?___
2 Our fa-thers when they prayed to you in ev-ery need, in ev-ery prayer,
MEN 3 But now my peo-ple turn on me with hate, not pi-ty, in their eyes;___

— Must I, a-lone un-ans-wered, go like one un-loved, a-lone to die?
— were heard by you and saved by you, and ne-ver doubt-ed that you care!
— and all who see me, see in me no man, a worm that they des-pise!

WOMEN
4 Let God deliver him, they say;
his God would save him, was his claim!
They only wait to see me die;
they share my clothing in a game!

MEN
5 My hands and feet they bind to wound;
my bones they number, and each breath,
until with burning thirst I taste
the bitter agony of death!

WOMEN
6 My God, I trust you, trust you still –
be near, be near to hear my prayer!
I know that all who hope in you
are safe in death from death's despair.

ALL
7 Then I and all who live for you,
this day and till the end of days,
will tell of ever-answered prayer,
and pray this world's most thankful praise!

Why, God, have you forsaken me 22A(ii)

Ombersley 8 8 8 8 (LM)

Words: Brian Foley
Music: W H Gladstone (1840–1891)

1 Why, God, have you for - sa - ken me – more dis - tant now the more I cry? Must I, a - lone un - ans - wered, go like one un - loved, a - lone to die?

2 Our fa - thers when they prayed to you in ev - ery need, in ev - ery prayer, were heard by you and saved by you, and ne - ver doubt - ed that you care!

MEN 3 But now my peo - ple turn on me with hate, not pi - ty, in their eyes; and all who see me, see in me no man, a worm that they des - pise!

WOMEN
4 Let God deliver him, they say;
his God would save him, was his claim!
They only wait to see me die;
they share my clothing in a game!

MEN
5 My hands and feet they bind to wound;
my bones they number, and each breath,
until with burning thirst I taste
the bitter agony of death!

WOMEN
6 My God, I trust you, trust you still –
be near, be near to hear my prayer!
I know that all who hope in you
are safe in death from death's despair.

ALL
7 Then I and all who live for you,
this day and till the end of days,
will tell of ever-answered prayer,
and pray this world's most thankful praise!

43

23A(i) The Lord my shepherd rules my life

Bedfordshire May-Day Carol 8 6 8 6 (CM)

Words: from Psalm 23
Christopher Idle
Music: English traditional melody
arranged Paul Edwards

1 The__ Lord my__ shep - herd__ rules my__ life and__
gives me all I__ need;_____ he leads me__ by re -
- fresh - ing__ streams, in pas - tures__ green I__ feed.

2 The__ Lord re - vives__ my__ fail - ing__ strength, he__
makes my joy com - plete;_____ and in right__ paths, for__
his__ name's sake, he__ guides my__ falter - ing__ feet.

3 Though in a__ val - ley__ dark as__ death, no__
e - vil makes me__ fear;_____ your shep - herd's staff pro -
- tects__ my__ way, for you are__ with me__ there.

4 While all my enemies look on
  you spread a royal feast;
  you fill my cup, anoint my head,
  and treat me as your guest.

5 Your goodness and your gracious love
  pursue me all my days;
  your house, O Lord, shall be my home –
  your name, my endless praise.

6 To Father, Son and Spirit, praise!
  to God, whom we adore,
  be worship, glory, power and love,
  both now and evermore!

The Lord my shepherd rules my life 23A(ii)

Brother James' Air 8 6 8 6 8 6

Words: from Psalm 23
Christopher Idle
Music: J L Macbeth Bain (c1840–1925)
arranged John Barnard

1 The Lord my shep-herd rules my life and__ gives me all I__ need;
2 The Lord re-vives my__ fail-ing strength, he__ makes my joy com-plete;
3 Though in a val-ley__ dark as death, no__ e-vil makes me__ fear;

he leads me by__ re-fresh-ing streams, in__ pas-tures green I__ feed;
and in right paths, for__ his name's sake, he__ guides my fal-tering feet;
your shep-herd's staff pro-tects my way, for__ you are with me__ there;

he leads me by re-fresh-ing streams, in pas-tures green I feed.
and in right paths, for his name's sake, he guides my fal-tering feet.
your shep-herd's staff pro-tects my way, for you are with me there.

4 While all my enemies look on
you spread a royal feast;
you fill my cup, anoint my head,
and treat me as your guest;
    you fill my cup, anoint my head,
    and treat me as your guest.

5 Your goodness and your gracious love
pursue me all my days;
your house, O Lord, shall be my home –
your name, my endless praise;
    your house, O Lord, shall be my home –
    your name, my endless praise.

6 To Father, Son and Spirit, praise!
to God, whom we adore,
be worship, glory, power and love,
both now and evermore;
    be worship, glory, power and love,
    both now and evermore!

Alternative tune: Shoreham-by-Sea, *Songs from the Psalms* 23A

23B   O Lord my Shepherd, lead me

Willard   10 10 10 10

Words: from Psalm 23
Pearl Beasley
Music: Keith Landis
arranged Peter Cutts

1 O Lord my shep-herd, lead me in your ways
2 When deep-est dark-ness falls a-round my head,
3 You wel-come me to share the ho-ly feast,

to cool-ing streams where I shall drink and live;
I need not fear with you close by my side;
you of-fer me for-give-ness and your love;

to pas-tures green where I may spend my days
and all a-long the sto-ny road I tread
and with your good-ness all my days are blessed —

in per-fect peace that on-ly you can give.
you will be there to strength-en and to guide.
un-til at last I reach your home a-bove.

Alternative tune: Eventide, *Hymns for Today's Church* 425

The Lord is my Shepherd

23C

Words: Psalm 23
from *The Liturgical Psalter*
David Frost and others
Music: T A Walmisley (1814–1856)

1 The Lord ˡ is my ˡ shepherd:
   therefore ˡ can I ˡ lack ˡ nothing.
2 He will make me lie down in ˡ green ˡ pastures:
   and ˡ lead me · beˡside still ˡ waters.

3 He will reˡfresh my ˡ soul:
   and guide me in right pathways ˡ for his ˡ name's ˡ sake.
4 Though I walk through the valley of the shadow of death
   I will ˡ fear no ˡ evil:
   for you are with me
   your ˡ rod · and your ˡ staff ˡ comfort me.

5 You spread a table before me
   in the face of ˡ those who ˡ trouble me:
   you have anointed my head with oil ˡ and my ˡ cup · will be ˡ full.
6 Surely your goodness and loving-kindness will follow me *
   all the ˡ days · of my ˡ life:
   and I shall dwell in the ˡ house · of the ˡ Lord for ˡ ever.

   Glory to the Father and ˡ to the ˡ Son:
   and ˡ to the ˡ Holy ˡ Spirit;
   as it was in the beˡginning · is ˡ now:
   and shall be for ˡ ever. ˡ Aˡmen.

24A

Lift up your heads

Wootton 8 6 8 6 (CM)

Words: from Psalm 24
David Mowbray
Music: Paul Edwards

1 Lift up your heads, e - ter - nal gates:___ the
2 What mor - tal dare as - cend___ God's hill___ or
3 Yes, all the earth is God's___ a - lone,___ its

Lord___ our God___ draws near; the King of glo - ry
reach___ that ho - ly place? Not those who plan their
com - pass far___ and wide, and in that King___ up -

now___ a - waits, his hosts___ in strength ap - pear.
neigh - bours ill and bring___ them to___ dis - grace.
- on___ the throne our trust___ and hope___ re - side.

Alternative tune: Nativity, *Hymns for Today's Church* 206

Fling wide the gates

Crucifer   10 10 and refrain

Words: from Psalm 24
Michael Perry
Music: S H Nicholson (1875–1947)

UNISON

Fling wide the gates, un-bar the an-cient doors; sa-

Fine

- lute your king_____ in his_____ tri - um - phant cause!

HARMONY

1 Now__ all the world__ be - longs to Christ our Lord: let__
2 Who__ has the right__ to__ wor - ship him to - day? All__
3 He__ comes to save__ all__ those who trust his name, and__
4 Who__ is the vic - tor__ glor - ious from the fight? He__

D.C.

all___ cre - a - tion__ greet the liv - ing Word!
those__ who__ glad - ly__ serve him and o - bey.
will__ de - clare__ them__ free from guilt and shame.
is__ our__ king,__ our__ life, our Lord, our right!

The earth is the Lord's

Words: Psalm 24
from *The Liturgical Psalter*
David Frost and others
Music: J Barnby (1838–1896)

1 The earth is the Lord's and ¦ all · that is ¦ in it:
   the compass of the ¦ world and ¦ those who ¦ dwell therein.
2 For he has founded it up ¦ on the ¦ seas:
   and es¦tablished it · up¦on the ¦ waters.
3 Who shall ascend the ¦ hill · of the ¦ Lord:
   or who shall ¦ stand · in his ¦ holy ¦ place?
4 He that has clean hands and a ¦ pure ¦ heart:
   who has not set his soul upon idols
   nor ¦ sworn his ¦ oath · to a ¦ lie.
5 He shall receive ¦ blessing · from the ¦ Lord:
   and recompense from the ¦ God of ¦ his sal¦vation.
6 Of such a kind as this are ¦ those who ¦ seek him:
   those who seek your ¦ face O ¦ God of ¦ Jacob.

7 Lift up your heads O you gates
   and be lifted up you ever¦lasting ¦ doors:
   and the King of ¦ glory ¦ shall come ¦ in.
8 Who is the ¦ King of ¦ glory?
   the Lord strong and mighty *
   the ¦ Lord ¦ mighty · in ¦ battle.

9 Lift up your heads O you gates
   and be lifted up you ever¦lasting ¦ doors:
   and the King of ¦ glory ¦ shall come ¦ in.
10 Who is the ¦ King of ¦ glory?
   the Lord of hosts ¦ he · is the ¦ King of ¦ glory.

   Glory to the Father and ¦ to the ¦ Son:
   and ¦ to the ¦ Holy ¦ Spirit;
   as it was in the be¦ginning · is ¦ now:
   and shall be for ¦ ever. ¦ A¦men.

All my soul to God I raise

St Petersburg 7 7 7 7 7 7

Words: from Psalm 25
Timothy Dudley-Smith
Music: D Bortnianski (1752–1825)

25A

1 All my soul to God I raise:
Be my guard-ian all my days.
Con-fi-dent in hope I rest,
Dai-ly prove your path is best.
Ev-er work in me your will,
Faith-ful to your pro-mise still.

2 Gra-cious-ly my sins for-give;
Help me by your truth to live.
In your foot-steps lead me, Lord,
Joy re-newed and hope re-stored,
Know-ing ev-ery sin for-given,
Learn-ing all the ways of heaven.

3 Mer-cies ma-ni-fold ex-tend,
Not as judge but faith-ful friend.
O my Sav-iour, hear my prayer,
Pluck my feet from ev-ery snare;
Qui-et-ude be mine at last,
Rest from all my guil-ty past.

4 Shel-tered safe when trou-bles fret,
Trust-ing God I tri-umph yet!
Un-dis-mayed in him I stand,
Vic-tor on-ly by his hand.
Wor-ship, hom-age, love and praise,
All my soul, to God I raise.

Following the psalmist, this text is abecedarian.
Alternative tune: Ratisbon, *Hymns for Today's Church* 266

26   To lead a blameless life

Talbot Woods 8 6 8 6 (CM)

Words: from Psalm 26
Michael Perry
Music: Michael Dawney

1 To lead a blame-less life, O Lord, to trust you with-out fear,
3 Let this be my su-preme de-sire, my ob - ject and my prayer,

to bring my hum-ble heart to you and know your love is near:
un - til I stand be - fore your throne to glo - ri - fy you there!

HARMONY

2 To walk be-fore you_ in the truth, to_ shun the e - vil ways,_

to come in - to your house to pray and_ shout a-loud your praise:

The Harmony version is not harmonically compatible with the Unison setting.

Alternative tune: St Peter, *Hymns for Today's Church* 211

God is my strong salvation

Christus der ist mein Leben 7 6 7 6

Words: from Psalm 27
J Montgomery (1771–1854)
Music: M Vulpius (c1560–1616)
arranged David Iliff

1 God is my strong salvation — what
2 Though hosts en - camp a - round me, firm
3 Place on the Lord re - li - ance, my
4 His might my heart shall strength - en, his

foe have I to fear? In dark - ness and temp -
to the fight I stand! What ter - ror can con -
soul, with cour - age wait — his truth my re - as -
love my joy in - crease; mer - cy my days shall

- ta - tion my light, my help is near:
- found me, with God at my right hand?
- sur - ance when faint and de - sol - ate:
length - en, the Lord will give me peace.

O Lord, my rock

Somerset 8 6 8 8 6

Words: from Psalm 28
Michael Perry
Music: Somerset folk song
arranged David Iliff

1 O__ Lord, my rock, to__ you__ I__ cry when o - thers will not__
2 I__ grieve for those who__ keep_ fine friends but__ har - bour God - less__
3 Yet_ praise the Lord who__ comes at__ length, who_ comes to right the__

hear;_____ to__ you I lift my__ hands on high— your__
schemes;_____ who__ use your works for__ worth - less ends, to__
wrong:_____ to__ you our shep - herd and our strength be__

arms are al - ways near, O Lord, your_ arms are al - ways_ near.
squan - der on their dreams, O Lord, to__ squan - der on their_ dreams.
praise in joy - ful song, O Lord, be__ praise in joy - ful__ song!

O Lord, my rock

St Bernard 8 6 8 6 (CM)

Words: from Psalm 28
Michael Perry
Music: *Tochter Zion* Cologne 1741

1 O Lord, my rock, to____ you I cry when
2 I grieve for those who____ keep fine friends but
3 Yet praise the Lord who____ comes at length, who

o - thers will not hear; to you I lift my
har - bour God - less schemes; who use your works for
comes to right the wrong: to you our shep - herd

hands on high — your arms are al - ways____ near.
worth - less ends, to squan - der on their____ dreams.
and our strength be praise in joy - ful____ song!

Alternative tune: Nicolaus, *Psalms for Today* 157A, *Hymns for Today's Church* 606

Let all in heaven and earth unite

Luther 8 7 8 7 8 8 7

Words: from Psalm 29
Basil Bridge
Music: *Geistliche Lieder* Wittenberg 1535

1 Let all in heaven and earth un - ite in this, our joy - ful du - ty; to praise our God, the Lord of might, the source of truth and beau - ty; the rumb - ling thun - der's awe - some voice, the light-ning flash, both cry, 'Re - joice! Come, give him praise and glo - ry!'

2 God's voice is e - choed by the seas, in storms, their power un - furl - ing, in winds that lash the ce - dar trees and set the de - sert swirl - ing; it stirs the migh - ty o - cean deep, the hills like star - tled cat - tle leap: come, give him praise and glo - ry!

Alternative tune: Palace Green, *Psalms for Today* 16A, *Hymns for Today's Church* 189

I worship you, O Lord

30A

Bishop Tucker 6 6 6 6 6 6

Words: from Psalm 30
J E Seddon (1915–1983)
Music: Norman Warren

1 I worship you, O Lord, for you have raised me up; I
WOMEN 2 Sing prais-es to the Lord, all those who know his name: for
MEN 3 I said, 'I am so strong I ne-ver shall be moved!' But
ALL 4 My mourn-ing you have turned to danc-ing and to joy; my

cried to you for help, and you re-stored my life. You
while his wrath is brief, his fav-our knows no end. Though
you, Lord, shook my life my heart was in dis-tress. I
sad-ness you dis-pelled as glad-ness filled my soul. And

brought me back from death and saved me from the grave.
tears may flow at night, the morn-ing brings new joy.
cried for you to help and plead-ed for your grace:
so I'll sing your praise, my God, through all my days!

31A   I come to you for shelter, Lord

Ye banks and braes 8 8 8 8 D (DLM)

Words: from Psalm 31
Basil Bridge
Music: Scottish traditional melody
arranged David Iliff

1 I come to you___ for shel - ter,
2 Your stead - fast love___ is my___ de -

Lord:___ de - liv - er me___ from ev - ery
-fence,___ my ha - ven from___ the strife___ of

snare. In you___ I find___ true li - ber -
tongues. You see___ my need,___ you hear___ my

- ty;___ I rest___ my spi - rit in___ your care. Your
cry,___ you turn___ my sor - rows in - to songs. May

lov - ing - kind - ness cheers my heart;___ you
all your peo - ple glad - ly come,___ and

know___ the hurts,___ the deep___ dis - tress! My
seek - ing, find___ you and___ a - dore: to

times___ are in___ your hand =___ I trust___ your
Fa - ther, Son___ and Spi - rit give___ all

ne - ver - fail - ing faith - ful - ness.
praise___ and glo - ry ev - er - more.

32A(i) How glad are those with peace of mind

Buttermere 8 8 8 8 (LM)

Words: from Psalm 32
David Mowbray
Music: John Barnard

UNISON

1 How glad are those with peace of mind, their past wrong-
(2 While ev-ery) wrong lay un-con-fessed, their spi-rits
(3 With your great) wis-dom, Lord, we pray, help us to

-do-ings left be-hind; their sins for-giv-en by the Lord — they stand, re-
knew no last-ing rest; but shed-ding tears of hon-es-ty they reached the
walk life's path to-day! How glad are those with peace of mind, their past wrong-

vv 1 and 2

-joic-ing in their God! 2 While ev-ery -do-ings left be-hind!
place of heart-felt joy. 3 With your great

v 3

How glad are those with peace of mind 32A(ii)

Hawkhurst 8 8 8 8 (LM)

Words: from Psalm 32
David Mowbray
Music: H J Gauntlett (1805–1876)

1 How glad are those with peace of mind, their
2 While ev - ery wrong lay un - con - fessed, their
3 With your great wis - dom, Lord, we pray, help

past wrong - do - ings left be - hind; their sins for - giv - en
spi - rits knew no last - ing rest; but shed - ding tears of
us to walk life's path to - day! How glad are those with

by the Lord — they stand, re - joic - ing in their God!
hon - es - ty they reached the place of heart - felt joy.
peace of mind, their past wrong - do - ings left be - hind!

Alternative tune: St Laurence, *Hymns for Today's Church* 133

33A   Bring songs of joy to God

Lardergate   8 8 8 8 8 8

Words: from Psalm 33
Paul Wigmore
Music: Stephen Matthews

1 Bring songs of joy to God the Lord who saves and keeps you by his
word; bring all your skill to harp and lyre, delight the
Lord with purest sound; let music high to heaven rebound, your praising hearts a joyful choir.

2 The Lord's own word is right and true, unfaithful deeds he will not
do; his justice, righteousness and love flow freely
from his gracious hand, enriching life till all the
land reveals a holy treasure trove.

3 By merest breath he brought to birth the starlit skies about the
earth; to him, the oceans vast and wild are in their
raging little more than water gathered in a
store or given to a thirsty child.

4 Come, fear the Lord! Hope in his love,
revere his word, his mercy prove;
then you will know his power to save,
to overrule the evil plan.
His watching eyes, since earth began,
care for the lives whose breath he gave.

5 With songs of joy to God the Lord
who saves and keeps us by his word
we bring our voices, harp and lyre
whose music shall to heaven rebound.
We trust in God: in him is found
true love that sets our hearts on fire.

Alternative tune: Surrey, *Hymns for Today's Church* 117

Tell his praise

Alleluia 8 7 8 7 D

Words: from Psalm 34
Timothy Dudley-Smith
Music: S S Wesley (1810–1876)

1 Tell his praise in song and sto - ry, bless the Lord with heart and voice:
2 To the Lord whose love has found them cry the poor in their dis - tress;
3 Taste and see! In faith draw near him, trust the Lord with all your powers;
4 In our need he walks be - side us, ears a - lert to ev - ery cry;

in my_ God is all my glo - ry, come be - fore him and re - joice.
swift his_ an - gels camped a - round them prove him_ sure to save and bless.
seek and_ serve him, love and fear him, life and_ all its joys are_ ours —
watch - ful_ eyes to guard and guide us, love that_ whis - pers, 'It is_ I.'

Join to praise his name to - ge - ther, he who hears his peo - ple's cry;
God it is who hears our cry - ing though the_ spark of faith be dim:
true de - light in ho - ly liv - ing, peace and_ plen - ty, length of days:
Good shall tri - umph, wrong be right - ed, God has pledged his pro - mised word;

tell his praise, come wind or_ wea - ther, shin - ing fa - ces_ lift - ed high.
taste and see! Be - yond de - ny - ing blessed are those who trust in_ him.
come, my child - ren, with thanks - giv - ing bless the Lord in_ songs of_ praise.
so with ran - somed saints u - ni - ted join to praise our_ liv - ing Lord.

Alternative tune: Wealdstone, *Hymns for Today's Church* 41

34B   I'll praise the Lord

Great Cheverell   10 10 7 8 10

Words: from Psalm 34
Paul Wigmore
Music: John Barnard

1 I'll praise the Lord for ev - er and
2 I sought the Lord, he an - swered my
3 O taste and see how gra - cious the
4 The Lord re - deems the faith - ful who

ev - er, my soul shall_ boast of his won - der - ful name:
call - ing, de - liv - ered_ me from my in - ner-most fears:
Lord___ is - se - cure are_ they who take re - fuge in him:
serve___ him, and those who_ trust him he ne - ver con-demns:

Glo - ri - fy the Lord with me; ex - alt his name, for great is he! I'll
great_ is___ he!

praise the Lord for ev - er and ev - er.

before verse 2

mp

before verse 3

p

before verse 4

f

after verse 4

ff

molto rall.

36   No fear of God

Sherington 8 6 8 8 6

Words: from Psalm 36
Christopher Idle
Music: Paul Edwards

1 No fear of God be-fore the eyes,____ no pe-ni-tence with-
2 Your love, O Lord, shall ne-ver sleep,____ nor shall your mer-cy
3 Be-neath the sha-dow of your wings____ our re-fuge is most
4 Con-ti-nue, Lord, your love to me,____ for you are all my

-in:____ such is the one no long-er wise, whose
cease;____ your truth is like the migh-ty deep, and
sure;____ re-freshed by your re-viv-ing springs and
trust;____ grant us the light we need, to see how

words are trea-che-ry and lies, who ne-ver grieves for sin.
like the rock-y moun-tain steep your stead-fast right-eous-ness.
all the joy your mer-cy brings our fu-ture is se-cure.
good you are, and still shall be to those you count as just.

Alternative tune: Binney's, *Hymns for Today's Church* 553

Commit your way to God

Summercourt 8 8 8 8 (LM)

Words: from Psalm 37
Michael Perry
Music: English traditional melody
arranged David Iliff

1 Com - mit your way to God the Lord – your
2 Be still be - fore the Lord and wait, and
3 Sal - va - tion comes from God a - lone – the
4 Com - mit your way to God the Lord, to

cause will shine as bright as fire; de - light to do God's
do not fret when wrong suc - ceeds; re - frain from an - ger,
faith - ful know their help is sure; to hea - ven all our
peace and truth and grace as - pire: then mer - cy shall be

ho - ly word and you shall find what you de - sire.
turn from hate, for God will pun - ish ev - il deeds.
needs are known, and in God's strength we are se - cure.
your re - ward, God's pro - mis - es your heart's de - sire.

Alternative tune: Wareham, *Hymns for Today's Church* 331

38   Lord, will you turn from your anger

Langleigh   11 10 11 10

Words: from Psalm 38
Mollie Knight
Music: Kenneth W Coates

UNISON

1 Lord, will you turn from your an - ger and hear me? Guilt and re-morse are the
2 Lord, though my friends and com - pan - ions de - sert me; you will not leave me – I
3 Lord, will you an - swer with words of for-give - ness? Then shall my joy and my

bur - dens I bear; When I ack - now - ledge my
know you are near. Hear my deep sigh - ing, and
peace be re - stored: faith - ful re - deem - er and

sin and my fol - ly, show your com-pas - sion, your love and your care.
see my great sor - row – you know each se - cret, each long - ing, each fear.
God of all com - fort, you are my sav - iour, my king and my Lord!

Alternative tune: O quanta qualia, *Hymns for Today's Church* 252

Silent, I have waited

Joyous Peace   6 5 6 5 D

Words: from Psalm 39
David Mowbray
Music: Hu Te-ai
arranged John Barnard

1 Si-lent, I have wait-ed, count-ing out my days;
2 Suf-fering, lea-den-weight-ed, drags my spi-rit low:

ques-tions o-ver-whelm me, set my heart a-blaze.
God in heaven, have mer-cy, let your heal-ing flow!

Mea-sured by God's great-ness hu-man lives are small;
All my hope I fast-en on your strength-ening word =

wealth de-parts, and beau-ty like a flower will fall.
lift your hand in bless-ing, let my prayer be heard!

Alternative tune: North Coates, *Psalms for Today* 162B(ii), *Hymns for Today's Church* 384

40A · To the Lord I looked

Nannerch 8 7 8 7 8 7

Words: from Psalm 40
Paul Wigmore
Music: John Barnard

1 To the Lord I looked in pa - tience from the dark - est pit of
2 For the Lord I wait-ed, trust - ing; then he turned his lov - ing
3 O how blessed, my God and Sav - iour, we who trust your migh - ty

clay, for he dai - ly proves his mer - cy, hears my call from far a -
eye, gent-ly lift - ed me to safe - ty on the rock se - cure and
hand! O how ma - ny are the won - ders which for us your love has

- way. And I tell the great as - sem - bly of his good - ness night and day.
high. And a hymn of praise he gave me— I shall sing it till I die:
planned! So shall all who seek and find_ you sing your praise through all the land.

Alternative tune: Mannheim, *Hymns for Today's Church* 525

Like the deer

Howerton 8 8 7 7

From Psalm 42
Words and music: Keith Landis
Music arranged David Iliff

1 Like the deer, a - thirst and quest - ing, seeks my
2 Why on earth should I be fear - ful, fool - ish -
3 Hope in him, for you will sure - ly taste that

soul for God, un - rest - ing, wide a - wake or in my
- ly down - cast and tear - ful? In my Sav - iour I have
ri - ver flow - ing pure - ly, bright as crys - tal from his

dreams, long - ing for life - giv - ing streams.
found God who keeps me safe and sound.
throne, God for ev - er seen and known!

42B

O put your trust in God

Tamié Tone

Words: from Psalm 42
from *The Liturgical Psalter*
David Frost and others
Music: Tamié tone
arranged Anthony Greening

Music arrangement: © Anthony Greening

O put your trust in God the living God:
I'll praise him yet, my saviour and my God.

1   As a deer longs for the ˈ running ˈ brooks:
    so longs my soul for ˈ you O ˈ God.
    My soul is thirsty for God * thirsty for the ˈ living ˈ God:
    when shall I come and ˈ see his ˈ face?
       O put your trust . . .

2   My tears have been my food ˈ day and ˈ night:
    while they ask me all day long 'Where now ˈ is your ˈ God?'
    Why are you so full of ˈ heaviness · my ˈ soul:
    and why so unˈquiet withˈin me?
       O put your trust . . .

3   Surely the Lord will grant his loving mercy ˈ in the ˈ day-time:
    and in the night his song will be with me
    a prayer to the ˈ God · of my ˈ life.
    Why are you so full of ˈ heaviness · my ˈ soul:
    and why so unˈquiet withˈin me?
       O put your trust . . .

O Light and Truth of God

Norwich 6 7 6 7 8 7

From Psalm 43
Words and music: Keith Landis
Music arranged Jeffrey Rickard

1 O___ Light and Truth of God, the world is dark a-
2 O___ high and ho-ly hill, O land of peace and
3 Be___ not cast down my soul, go to his al-tar

-round me; deep___ pit-falls, bat-tle-fields, and mor-tal
rest-ing— God's love-ly dwel-ling place, the goal of
sing-ing, with___ in-stru-ment_ and voice your gift of

foes_____ sur-round me: you are my Way as
all_____ my quest-ing: in you I'll find a
mu-sic bring-ing; e-ter-nal joy my

bright as day— all oth-er ways con-found me!
home as-signed, a man-sion for my guest-ing!
lips' em-ploy with al-le-lu-ias ring-ing!

When my bitter foes surround

43B

Carsaig 7 7 7 5

Words: from Psalm 43
Michael Perry
Music: G Thalben-Ball (1896–1987)

1 When my bit – ter foes___ sur - round,___ when their
2 When deep sor - rows o - ver - power,___ when life's
3 Then shall fer - vent prayers a - vail,___ then shall

wick – ed deeds___ con - found, when de - ceit___ and
pain___ and doubt___ de - vour, when I face___ my
light___ and truth pre - vail, then God's mer - cy

lies___ a - bound, I___ will hope__ in God.___
dark – est hour,___ I___ will trust__ in God.___
will___ not fail:___ I___ will praise__ my God.___

Alternative tune: Capetown, *Psalms for Today* 124A(ii), *Hymns for Today's Church* 12

44   We have heard, O Lord our God

Great Glen   7 6 8 8 6

Words: from Psalm 44
Michael Perry
Music: Peter White

1 We have heard,   O Lord our God,   the sto - ry of your
2 You are great,   O Lord our God,   we trust - ed in your
3 Yet to - day,   O Lord our God,   the weak – who once were

grace: and how you gave to us this land,   de - fend - ing
name;   we did not tri - umph by the sword,   but through the
strong –   cry out to you, 'O come, a - rise,   re - veal your

us with your right hand   and show - ing us   your face.
vic - tory of your word   you put our foes   to shame.
light to dark-ened eyes,   and turn our sighs   to song!'

Alternative tune: *Songs from the Psalms* 44

Let those with voices sing

Marlborough Gate 6 6 6 6 8 8

Words: from Psalm 45
David Mowbray
Music: Wayne Marshall

1 Let those with voi - ces sing, as if in - spired to write the prais - es of our king, our heart and soul's de - light:

2 With scep - tre in his hand our king will reign in peace; no e - vil can with - stand his sword of right - eous - ness.

3 A - noint - ed thus to serve, and set a - part on high, our king yet stoops to love, to hear his peo - ple's cry. Be - fore his throne the

4 So let his pa - lace ring with roy - al praise to - day; let sons and daugh - ters bring their gifts with - out de - lay! na - tions fall and throng to crown him Lord of all.

Alternative tune: Gopsal, *Psalms for Today* 47A, *Hymns for Today's Church* 180

Music: © Wayne Marshall

Words: © David Mowbray/Jubilate Hymns †

46A God is our strength and refuge

Dam Busters March 7 7 7 5 7 7 11

Words: from Psalm 46
Richard Bewes
Music: E Coates (1886–1958)
arranged John Barnard

UNISON

1 God is our strength and re-fuge, our pres-ent help in trou-ble;

and we there-fore will not fear, though the earth should change!

Though moun-tains shake and trem-ble, though swirl-ing floods are rag-ing,

God the Lord of hosts is with us ev-er-more!

The Harmony version is harmonically compatible with the Unison setting.

79

God is our refuge and strength

46B

Words: Psalm 46
from *The Liturgical Psalter*
David Frost and others
Music: Martin Luther (1483–1546)
Descant: S H Nicholson (1875–1947)

DESCANT

The Lord of hosts is with us: the God of Ja - cob is our stronghold.

1 God is our ¦ refuge · and ¦ strength:
  a very ¦ present ¦ help in ¦ trouble.
2 Therefore we will not fear though the ¦ earth be ¦ moved:
  and though the mountains are ¦ shaken · in the ¦ midst · of the ¦ sea;

Second part
3 though the waters ¦ rage and ¦ foam:
  and though the mountains quake at the ¦ rising ¦ of the ¦ sea.

4 There is a river whose streams make glad the ¦ city · of ¦ God:
  the holy dwelling-place ¦ of the ¦ Most ¦ High.
5 God is in the midst of her
  therefore she shall ¦ not be ¦ moved:
  God will ¦ help her · and at ¦ break of ¦ day.

6 The nations make uproar and the ¦ kingdoms · are ¦ shaken:
  but God has lifted his ¦ voice · and the ¦ earth shall ¦ tremble.
7 **The Lord of ¦ hosts is ¦ with us:**
  the God of ¦ Jacob ¦ is our ¦ stronghold.

8 Come then and see what the ¦ Lord has ¦ done:
  what destruction he has ¦ brought up¦on the ¦ earth.
9 He makes wars to cease in ¦ all the ¦ world:
  he breaks the bow and shatters the spear
  and burns the ¦ chari·ots ¦ in the ¦ fire.

10 'Be still and know that ¦ I am ¦ God:
  I will be exalted among the nations
  I will be ex¦alted · up¦on the ¦ earth.'
11 **The Lord of ¦ hosts is ¦ with us:**
  the God of ¦ Jacob ¦ is our ¦ stronghold.

  Glory to the Father and ¦ to the ¦ Son:
  and ¦ to the ¦ Holy ¦ Spirit;
  as it was in the be¦ginning · is ¦ now:
  and shall be for ¦ ever. ¦ A¦men.

Take heart and praise our God

Gopsal 6 6 6 6 8 8

Words: from Psalm 47
David Mowbray
Music: melody and bass G F Handel (1685–1759)

1 Take heart and praise our God; re - joice and clap your
2 Take heart, but sing with fear, ex - alt his wor - thy
3 Take heart for fu - ture days, for tasks as yet un -
4 Take heart and trust in God the Fa - ther and the

hands – his power our foe sub - dued, his
name; with mind a - lert and clear his now
- known – the God whose name we praise is
Son – God is our strength and shield, his

mer - cy ev - er stands:
ce - le - brate his fame: let trum - pets sound and
seat - ed on the throne:
Spi - rit guides us on:

peo - ple sing, the Lord through all the earth is king!

47B God is the king of all the earth

Words: from Psalm 47
from *The Liturgical Psalter*
David Frost and others
Music: John Barnard

1st time: CHOIR God is the king of all the earth – O
2nd time: ALL

praise him in a well-wrought psalm.   CHOIR 1 O

clap your hands, all you peo – ples, __ and cry a-loud to God with shouts of joy:_ for the Lord Most High is to be feared – he is a great king o - ver all____ the earth.

ALL God is the king of all the earth – O praise him in a well-wrought psalm.

CHOIR 2 He cast down peo-ples un - der us,_ and the na - tions be -

-neath our feet; he chose us a land for our pos-ses - sion that was the pride of

Ja - cob whom__ he loved. ALL God is the king of

all the earth – O praise him in a well-wrought psalm.

CHOIR 3 God has gone up__ with the sound of re - joic - ing, and the Lord_ to the blast of the horn: O sing prais - es, sing

prais-es to God;_ O sing prais - es, sing prais - es to____ our

King. ALL God is the king of all the earth — O

praise him in a well-wrought psalm.

DESCANT 2nd time

Great is the Lord

La Corbière 8 8 8 8 (LM)

Words: from Psalm 48
Christopher Idle
Music: Norman Warren

1 Great is the Lord! His praise is great on Zi - on's
2 God is the Tower whose strength was shown when Sa - tan's
3 Our ears have heard, our eyes have seen what God the

mount, his ho - ly place; the roy - al ci - ty crowns the
ar - mies threat - ened harm; they gath - ered round, and looked, and
Lord of Hosts has done; with - in these walls we ce - le -

earth and shines on all with ra - diant grace.
ran like boats be - fore the driv - ing storm.
- brate his stead - fast love, his age - less throne.

4 God is the Judge whose mighty name
across the world with praise shall ring:
for his resplendent victories
let Zion shout and Judah sing!

5 God is the King whose kingdom's power
we see built up on every side;
we tell our children of our God
who will for ever be our Guide.

Alternative tune: Truro, *Hymns for Today's Church* 31

What riches on this earth

Golden Hill 6 6 8 6 (SM)

Words: from Psalm 49
Paul Wigmore
Music: *Kentucky Harmony* 1816
arranged David Iliff

1 What rich - es___ on this earth___ can
2 What wis - dom___ in this life___ can
3 What rich - es___ come from God___ when
4 And wis - dom___ I shall know___ when

buy one___ hu - man breath?___ No wealth brings im - mor -
know the___ mind of God?___ No sage can___ tread the
his de - sire is mine;___ his will un - locks a
he re - deems my soul;___ for at his___ throne the

-ta - li - ty, no trea - sure___ hin - ders___ death.___
paths of___ thought where our Cre - a - tor___ trod.___
trea - su - ry, his love re - veals___ a___ shrine!___
mor - tal___ mind is sanc - ti - fied___ and___ whole.___

Alternative tune: Franconia, *Hymns for Today's Church* 110

Music arrangement: © David Iliff/Jubilate Hymns †

Words: © Paul Wigmore/Jubilate Hymns †

O people, listen

Wharfdale 11 10 11 10

Words: from Psalm 49
Michael Perry
Music: Norman Warren

Gently flowing

1 O peo - ple, lis - ten – hear God's wis - dom cry - ing!____ Al -
2 For God will take the ho - ly in - to hea - ven,____ by
3 To Fa - ther, Son and Spi - rit be the glo - ry!____ Come,

- though the dark - ness comes to rich and poor,____ and no - thing mor - tal can sur - vive our
grace re - deem the faith - ful from the grave;____ we leave be - hind us all this world has
wor - ship and a - dore the ho - ly Name;____ let wis - dom think up - on our hu - man

dy - ing,____ yet in the morn - ing jus - tice shall en - dure:
giv - en,____ and trust God's migh - ty power to love and save!
sto - ry,____ and faith our ev - er - liv - ing God pro - claim.

Alternative tune: Highwood, *Psalms for Today* 138A, *Hymns for Today's Church* 422

Let God, who called the worlds to be 50A

A babe is born 8 8 8 8 (LM)

Words: from Psalm 50
David Mowbray
Music: English traditional melody
arranged David Iliff

1 Let God, who called the worlds to be, a -rise in all - con - sum - ing fire to judge the peo - ple right - eous - ly, and faith - less ones with awe in - spire.

2 This God is ours, and yet we break the co - ve - nant made long a - go; God's words we fool - ish - ly for - sake, God's ways we have re - fused to know.

3 For though our lips have preached God's law, our err - ing hearts have scorned the Name; we choose the thief and slan - der - er as friends, and so in - crease our shame.

4 What then shall God the Lord de - mand? Not gifts or lav - ish of - fer - ing, but vows and pro - mis - es per - formed, and lives from which true prais - es spring!

Alternative tune: Solothurn, *Psalms for Today* 3A, *Hymns for Today's Church* 276

50B   God speaks – the Lord of all the earth

Christmas Eve   8 6 8 6 D (DCM)

Words: from Psalm 50
Michael Perry
Music: English traditional melody
arranged David Iliff

1 God speaks – the Lord of___ all the earth, and calls the world to hear:
2 'Yet___ hon-our me, ful - fil your vow, in truth pre-pare the road –

what glo - ry shines, what light springs forth, to draw the peo - ple near!
so___ to the faith - ful___ I will show the sav - ing grace of God.'

Says God, the right - eous one, the___ wise, 'Your wor-ship I de - cline;
Then lift your hearts and___ voi - ces___ high to___ Fa - ther and to Son

I have no need of___ sa - cri-fice for all the___ world is mine.'
and Spi - rit – Three in___ ma - jes-ty, our God for___ ev - er One!

God, be merciful to me

Aberystwyth 7 7 7 7 D

Words: from Psalm 51
adapted from *The Psalter* 1912
in this version Word & Music
Music: J Parry (1841–1903)

1 God, be mer - ci - ful to me, let your love my re - fuge be;
2 Wash me, wash me pure with - in, cleanse, O cleanse me from my sin:
3 Gra - cious God, my heart re - new, make my spi - rit right and true;

my of - fen - ces wash a - way, cleanse me from my sin to - day.
in your right - eous - ness I trust, in your judge - ments you are just.
from my sins O hide your face, blot them out in bound - less grace.

My trans - gres - sions I con - fess, grief and guilt my soul op - press;
Come, sal - va - tion to im - part, teach your wis - dom to my heart;
Cast your ser - vant not a - way, let your Spi - rit with me stay;

I have sinned a - gainst your grace and pro - voked you to your face.
make me pure, your grace be - stow, that your mer - cy I may know.
make me joy - ful, will - ing, strong, teach me your sal - va - tion's song!

51B   Have mercy on me O God

Words: from Psalm 51
from *The Liturgical Psalter*
David Frost and others
Music: David Iliff

Have mercy on me O God in your en'during ' goodness:
according to the fulness of your compassion * '
blot out ' my of'fences.
Wash me thoroughly ' from my ' wickedness:
and ' cleanse me ' from my ' sin.

For I acknowledge ' my re'bellion:
and my ' sin is ' ever · be'fore me.
Against you only have I sinned *
and done what is evil ' in your ' eyes:
so you will be just in your sentence
and ' blameless ' in your ' judging.

Purge me with hyssop and I ' shall be ' clean:
wash me and I ' shall be ' whiter · than ' snow.
Create in me a clean ' heart O ' God:
and re'new a · right ' spirit · with'in me.

Do not cast me ' out · from your ' presence:
do not take your ' holy ' spirit ' from me.
O give me the gladness of your ' help a'gain:
and sup'port me · with a ' willing ' spirit.

You take no pleasure in sacrifice or ' I would ' give it:
burnt ' offerings · you ' do not ' want.
The sacrifice of God is a ' broken ' spirit:
a broken and contrite heart O God ' you will ' not de'spise.

Glory to the Father and ' to the ' Son:
and ' to the ' Holy ' Spirit;
as it was in the be'ginning · is ' now:
and shall be for ' ever. ' A'men.

Music: © David Iliff/Jubilate Hymns †

Why in the dawning

Flanders 10 10 10 10

Words: from Psalm 52
Paul Wigmore
Music: David Iliff

52

1 Why in the dawn - ing of an - oth - er day does e - vil pierce the
2 Why through the glo - ry of an - oth - er day comes ra - zor - sharp the
3 Why at the even - ing of an - oth - er day should boast - ing pride de -
4 O God, cast out the sin that kills the soul, that brings your whole cre -

beau - ty we would see; when from the ne - ver - fail - ing grace of God
tongue that would de - stroy; when God, who at a word made all the earth,
- base the good and pure; when God him - self has blessed the con - trite heart
- a - tion in - to shame: and I through bright - est day and dark - est night

comes strength to make us flour - ish like a tree?
would be our cer - tain strong - hold and our joy?
and bless - ing, made the soul's re - demp - tion sure?
with all the saints will praise your ho - ly name!

Alternative tune: Farley Castle, *Hymns for Today's Church* 361

53 Only the fool will say

Astwood 10 10 10 10

Words: from Psalm 53
Michael Perry
Music: Paul Edwards

1 On - ly the fool will say 'There is no God'; on - ly the one whose
2 On - ly from Zi - on shall sal - va - tion come; on - ly in God we

way is full of lies: and God looks down in vain to see their
all may live in peace: lift high your voi - ces, sing God's wor - thy

love, for on - ly few re - main who do God's will.
praise, and on - ly serve your_ king who stoops to save.

Alternative tune: *Songs from the Psalms 53*

Save me, O God, hear my prayer

Heather 7 7 7 7

Words: from Psalm 54
Michael Perry
Music: Norman Warren

1 Save me, O God, hear my prayer, o - pen your
2 Yet shall the Lord be my help – strong is the

ears to my cry; keep me when e - vils pre -
one who sus - tains; offer - ings of love I will

- vail, strength - en my hand from on high.
bring God who e - tern - al - ly reigns!

54(ii) Save me, O God, hear my prayer

Knightwood 7 7 7 7

Words: from Psalm 54
Michael Perry
Music: Hugh Benham

1 Save me, O God, hear my prayer,   o - pen your ears   to my cry;
2 Yet shall the Lord be my help –   strong is the one who sus-tains;

keep   me when e - vils pre-vail,   strength-en my hand from on high.
offer - ings of love   I will bring   God who e - ter - nal - ly reigns!

O for the wings to fly afar

Shepherd Boy's Song   8 6 8 6 (CM)

Words: from Psalm 55
David Mowbray
Music: J H Alden (1900–1976)

1 O   for the wings   to   fly a - far   and
2 Of   all my pain, the deep - est wound was
3 God, take this bur - den that I bring,   and

like   a   dove   to   rest,____   to   live un - trou - bled
dealt   not by   some foe,____   but by my own fa -
help   me to   for - give;____   then with a light - er

by   the care which_ brings us   to____ the____ test.
- mi - liar friend with__ whom   I loved_ to____ go.
heart, I'll sing and__ to your glo - ry____ live!

Alternative tune: Metzler, *Hymns for Today's Church* 178

56A Be merciful to me, O God

Bangor 8 6 8 6 (CM)

Words: from Psalm 56
Paul Wigmore
Music: W Tans'ur's *Harmony of Syon* 1734

1 Be mer-ci-ful___ to me, O___ God— for
2 I fear the hurt-ful word of___ scorn, I
3 But when I am___ a-fraid, O___ God, I'll
4 My tears are gone = now lead me,___ Lord, de-

those_ who_ harm draw near; they_ turn my words of___
dread_ the_ mock-ing gaze, the_ deed that comes of___
put_ my_ trust in you: if___ God im-mor-tal
-fend_ me_ in the strife: for___ then in your great_

good_ in-tent, they_ fill my_ day with fear.
cru-el-ty, the_ hat-red_ it be-trays.
strength-ens_ me, what_ harm can_ mor-tals do?
strength I'll_ walk led_ by the_ Light of Life.

Be gracious to me, Lord

57A

Boundless love 6 6 8 6 (SM)

Words: from Psalm 57
Michael Perry
Music: Norman Warren
arranged John Barnard

1 Be gra - cious to me, Lord, _____ and
2 Though snares are set for me, _____ yet
3 My soul, a - wake and sing, _____ God's

hold my spi - rit fast, _____ that I may shel - ter
will I sleep in peace, _____ for I have asked the
bound - less love re - call; _____ ex - alt God's name a -

by your side un - til the storm is _____ past.
care of God whose love shall ne - ver _____ cease.
- bove the skies, God's glo - ry o - ver _____ all!

Alternative tune: Holyrood, *Hymns for Today's Church* 497

60   We are a land divided

Potterne 7 6 7 6 D

Words: from Psalm 60
Michael Perry
Music: John Barnard

UNISON

1 We are a land di-vid-ed, un-wor-thy of you,
Lord, and yet by your great mer-cy our peace can be re-
stored. Though we in-vite your an-ger and fail to do your
will, yet if we turn and fear you your love can tri-umph still.

2 Our God is strong to save us and tread the e-vil
down, to raise the cause of jus-tice and gain the vic-tor's
crown. Sing glo-ry to the Fa-ther, bring wor-ship to the
Son, a-dore the Ho-ly Spi-rit: praise God the Three-in-One!

Alternative tune: Aurelia, *Hymns for Today's Church* 501

Listen to my prayer, Lord

Listening 6 5 6 5

Words: from Psalm 61
J E Seddon (1915–1983)
Music: Norman Warren

1 Lis - ten to my prayer, Lord, hear my hum - ble
2 In earth's far - thest cor - ner you will hear my
MEN 3 You have been my shel - ter when the foe was

cry: when my heart is faint - ing,
voice: set me on your rock, Lord,
near, as a tower of re - fuge

vv 1-5 / v 6

to your throne I fly.
then I shall re - joice. be my songs of praise!
shield - ing me from fear.

WOMEN
4 I will rest for ever
in your care and love,
guarded and protected
as by wings above.

ALL
5 All that I have promised,
help me to fulfil;
and in all who love you
work your perfect will.

6 May your truth and mercy
keep me all my days;
let my words and actions
be my songs of praise!

Alternative tune: Caswall, *Hymns for Today's Church* 126 or *Songs from the Psalms* 61A

61B(i)   O God, hear me calling

Love's Gift   11 11 11 11

Words: from Psalm 61
Paul Wigmore
Music: English traditional melody
arranged David Iliff

1 O God, hear me calling and answer, I pray!
2 When trouble comes near me and enemies taunt,
3 For Lord you have heard all the vows I have made
4 I long for the day when your dwelling is mine,

No distance can silence the words that I say,
Lord, you are the fortress no evil can daunt;
my thoughts and intentions when homage I paid;
your wings for a shelter, your presence a shrine;

no mountain, no ocean can hinder my prayer
and safe on the rock that is higher than I
with all who have lived by the fear of your name,
I praise you on earth for your mercy and grace:

when deep is my sorrow and dark my despair.
your strength is my hope as you answer my cry.
Lord, grant all my prayers as your praise I proclaim.
what blessings I'll sing when I look on your face!

O God, hear me calling

61B(ii)

Stowey 11 11 11 11

Words: from Psalm 61
Paul Wigmore
Music: English traditional melody
arranged Norman Warren

1 O God, hear me calling and answer, I pray! No distance can silence the words that I say, no mountain, no ocean can hinder my prayer when deep is my sorrow and dark my despair.

2 When trouble comes near me and enemies taunt, Lord, you are the fortress no evil can daunt; and safe on the rock that is higher than I your strength is my hope as you answer my cry.

3 For Lord you have heard all the vows I have made – my thoughts and intentions when homage I paid; with all who have lived by the fear of your name, Lord, grant all my prayers as your praise I proclaim.

4 I long for the day when your dwelling is mine, your wings for a shelter, your presence a shrine; I praise you on earth for your mercy and grace: what blessings I'll sing when I look on your face!

62A
Rest in God

Michael 8 7 8 7 3 3 7

Words: from Psalm 62
David Mowbray
Music: Herbert Howells (1892–1983)

UNISON

1 Rest in God, our God_ most migh - ty_ thanks and praise to
2 Trust no more in doubt - ful_ rich - es, part with those who
3 In the past the Lord has_ spo - ken through his pro - phets
4 Glo - ry be to God_ the_ Fa - ther, glo - ry be to

him_ be - long; from the Lord comes our sal - va - tion,
work_ de - ceit: God him - self is our re - ward - er,
and_ the law, shin - ing lan - tern for our jour - ney,
God_ the Son, glo - ry be to God the Spi - rit -

he re - mains our strength and song. Si - lent - ly
throned up - on his judge - ment seat. Mer - cy waits
where no path was known be - fore. Hope a - gain!
ev - er Three and ev - er One. Trust God still,

none but_ he waits, our rock_ and shield_ to be.
at his_ gates for each one_ who false - hood hates.
Fears are_ vain_ God's re - new - ing power_ is plain.
do his_ will; hold to him through good_ and ill!

Music: © Novello & Co Ltd,
8/10 Lower James Street, London W1R 3PL

Words: © David Mowbray/Jubilate Hymns †

My soul is at rest in God

From Psalm 62
Taizé
Words and music: Jacques Berthier

62B

The accompaniment is suitable for the Verses as well as the Refrain.
The Refrain may be sung before and after each verse
or additionally as an accompaniment to each verse.

Words and music: © 1982, 1983 and 1984 Les Presses de Taizé (France)
Published by Wm Collins Sons & Co Ltd
(USA) GIA Publications,
7404 South Mason Avenue, Chicago, Illinois 60638

63A

God is my great desire

Leoni 6 6 8 4 D

Words: from Psalm 63
Timothy Dudley-Smith
Music: from a synagogue melody for the Yigdal (doxology)
transcribed M Lyon (1751–1797)
adapted T Olivers (1725–1799)

1 God is my great de - sire, his face I seek the first; to
2 God is my true de - light, my rich - est feast his praise, through
3 God is my strong de - fence in ev - ery e - vil hour; in

him my heart and soul a - spire, for him I thirst. As
si - lent watch - es of the night, through all my days. To
him I face with con - fi - dence the temp - ter's power. I

one in de - sert lands, whose ve - ry flesh is flame, in
him my spi - rit clings, on him my soul is cast; be -
trust his mer - cy sure, with truth and tri - umph crowned: my

burn - ing love I lift my hands and bless his name.
-neath the sha - dow of his wings he holds me fast.
hope and joy for ev - er - more in him are found.

O God, you are my God

63B

Temple Guiting   6 6 10 5

Words: from Psalm 63
Paul Wigmore
Music: John Barnard

1 O God, you are my God: I seek you with my heart;_____ my
2 O God, you are my God: your glo-ry I have seen;_____ with
3 O God, you are my God: I think of you at night;_____ with -

soul is thirs-ty for you in a dry_____ and wea-ry de - sert.
sing - ing shall my lips a - dore you, Lord,_____ and glo-ry give you.
- in the sha-dow of your wings I stay,_____ and you de - fend me.

4 O God, you are my God:
   the victory is yours;
   all evil by your justice overthrown
      in holy anger.

5 As long as I shall live
   my lips will sing your praise;
   my hungry soul will feast upon your love,
      and glorify you.

65A God whose praise is sung in Zion

Bennelong 878787

Words: from Psalm 65
David Mowbray
Music: Robert Boughen

UNISON

1 God whose praise is sung in Zi - on, Lord who
2 Vi - sit, Lord, the earth to bless it, pros - per
3 Glo - ry be to God the Fa - ther, glo - ry

calls the worlds to be; ma - ker of the
all the grow - ing corn; let the val - leys
be to God the Son, Glo - ry be to

moun-tain ran - ges, mas-ter of the roar-ing sea: we, with
fill with laugh - ter and the lambs be safe - ly born; crown the
God the Spi - rit, ev - er Three and ev - er One! Earth's cre -

saints of ev - ery na - tion, sing your praise, who sets us free.
farm-er's year with good - ness, till the days of plen-ty dawn!
- a - tor, Lord, life - giv - er, let your work through us be done!

Alternative tune: Rhuddlan, *Hymns for Today's Church* 195

You are to be praised O God

Words: from Psalm 65
from *The Liturgical Psalter*
David Frost and others
Music: G M Garrett (1834–1897)

65B

You are to be praised O ˈ God in ˈ Zion:
to you shall vows be paid ˈ you that ˈ answer ˈ prayer.
Those who dwell at the ends of the earth are aˈfraid at · your ˈ wonders:
the dawn and the ˈ evening ˈ sing your ˈ praises.

You tend the ˈ earth and ˈ water it:
you ˈ make it ˈ rich and ˈ fertile.
You crown the ˈ year · with your ˈ goodness:
and the tracks where you have ˈ passed ˈ drip with ˈ fatness.

The pastures of the ˈ wilderness · run ˈ over:
and the ˈ hills are ˈ girded · with ˈ joy.
The meadows are ˈ clothed with ˈ sheep:
and the valleys stand so thick with corn
they ˈ shout for ˈ joy and ˈ sing.

Glory to the Father and ˈ to the ˈ Son:
and ˈ to the ˈ Holy ˈ Spirit;
as it was in the beˈginning · is ˈ now:
and shall be for ˈ ever. ˈ Aˈmen.

66A Praise our God with shouts of joy

Harts 7 7 7 7

Words: from Psalm 66
Christopher Idle
Music: B Milgrove (1731–1810)

1 Praise our God with shouts of joy, sing the glo - ry____
2 Come and see what God has done by the power of____
3 God has tamed the rag - ing seas, carved a high - way____

of____ his name; join to____ lift his
his____ right hand; see the____ bat - tles
through__ the tide, paid the____ cost of

prais - es____ high, through the world his love____ pro - claim.
he has__ won by his word of swift__ com - mand.
our re - lease, come him - self to be____ our__ guide.

4 God has put us to the test,
bringing us through flood and fire
into freedom, peace, and rest,
for our good is his desire.

5 He has not despised my prayer
nor kept back his love from me;
he has raised me from despair –
to our God all glory be!

Words: © Christopher Idle/Jubilate Hymns †

Mercy, blessing, favour, grace

Urchfont 7 7 7 7

Words: from Psalm 67, *Deus misereatur*
Timothy Dudley-Smith
Music: John Barnard

1 Mer - cy, bless - ing, fa - vour, grace, sav - ing power to us be shown;
2 Shout in tri - umph, sing in praise! Peo - ples all, pro - claim his worth:
3 Har - vests year by year pro - claim bless-ings new in plen - ty poured;

bright - ness of the Fa - ther's face to the na - tions now be known.
just and right-eous are his ways, sov - ereign Lord of all the earth.
all the earth shall fear his name, all his peo - ple praise the Lord.

Alternative tune: Savannah, *Hymns for Today's Church* 150

May God be gracious

Universa Laus 10 10 10 10

Words: from Psalm 67, *Deus misereatur*
Stephen Horsfall
Music: Anthony Greening

1 May God be gra - cious, may we see his face;
2 He holds our fu - ture safe with - in his hand;

through-out the wide world may his power be known. May all the
he judg - es right - ly and he guides our ways. Earth yields its

na - tions trust his sav - ing grace, and come to wor - ship,__
in - crease — God will bless our land: may all his peo - ple,__

__ and come to wor - ship him__ be - fore his throne.
__ may all his peo - ple give__ him thanks and praise!

Original key: D♭
Alternative tunes: Ellers, *Hymns for Today's Church* 281, St Agnes, *Hymns for Today's Church* 406

Let God be gracious to us

Words: Psalm 67, *Deus misereatur*
from *The Liturgical Psalter*
David Frost and others
Music: J Nares (1715–1783)

1 Let God be gracious to ᐧ us and ᐧ bless us:
   and make his ᐧ face ᐧ shine upᐧon us,
2 that your ways may be ᐧ known on ᐧ earth:
   your liberating ᐧ power · aᐧmong all ᐧ nations.

3 Let the peoples ᐧ praise you · O ᐧ God:
   let ᐧ all the ᐧ peoples ᐧ praise you.
4 Let the nations be ᐧ glad and ᐧ sing:
   **for you judge the peoples with integrity
   and govern the ᐧ nations · upᐧon ᐧ earth.**

5 Let the peoples ᐧ praise you · O ᐧ God:
   let ᐧ all the ᐧ peoples ᐧ praise you.
6 Then the earth will ᐧ yield its ᐧ fruitfulness:
   and ᐧ God our ᐧ God will ᐧ bless us.

Second part
7 God ᐧ shall ᐧ bless us:
   and all the ᐧ ends · of the ᐧ earth will ᐧ fear him.

   **Glory to the Father and ᐧ to the ᐧ Son:
   and ᐧ to the ᐧ Holy ᐧ Spirit;
   as it was in the beᐧginning · is ᐧ now:
   and shall be for ᐧ ever. ᐧ Aᐧmen.**

DESCANT for verse 7

7 God   shall___ bless us: and all the   ends of the earth will   fear him.

Let God arise

Song 46   10 10

Words: from Psalm 68
Christopher Idle
Music: Orlando Gibbons (1583–1625)

ALL 1 Let God a - rise!___ his e - ne - mies be gone
WOMEN 2 Make known the Lord,___ and sound his name a - loud
MEN 3 Fa - ther and judge,___ he gave the world his law

and melt like wax be - fore the ho - ly One.
to praise the king who rides up - on the cloud.
with free - dom, love and jus - tice for the poor.

WOMEN
4 God marched ahead, strong shepherd of his flock;
the heavens opened; earth in terror shook.

MEN
5 God spoke the word, and faithful was the band
of those who took his truth to every land.

ALL
6 See God ascend, with captives as his prize,
and gifts for all who shall in him arise.

WOMEN
7 Bless day by day the living God who saves,
who raises up his people from their graves.

MEN
8 Draw near his throne: musicians lead our song!
all nations, tribes, and races join the throng.

WOMEN
9 All strength is his! the rebels reign no more;
he scatters all who take delight in war.

MEN
10 God rules on high, and mighty is his voice:
to God be praise; in God we shall rejoice.

ALL
11 Glory to God, creator, saviour, friend
whose greatness, love, and wisdom never end.

Verses with italicized numbers may be omitted.

When the waters cover me

Salvum me   7 4 7 7 7 4

Words: from Psalm 69
Michael Perry
Music: David Llewellyn Green

1 When the waters cover me, save me, O God; when I look and cannot see, when I seek what cannot be, when my friends abandon me, save me, O God.

2 You know all my guilty fears, thank you, O God, you have heard with open ears, you have seen my contrite tears, bless me all the years, thank you, O God.

May be sung a tone higher in G minor when performed by choir alone.

Come quickly, Lord

Splendour 8 8 8 8 (LM)

Words: from Psalm 70
Bert Polman
Music: M Praetorius (1571–1621)
adapted from *Piae Cantiones* 1582
arranged David Iliff

1 Come quick - ly, Lord, to res - cue
2 May all who seek your name re -
3 Yet I am poor and need - y,

me, and has - ten to my help, I
- joice, your praise in gra - ti - tude re -
Lord: be quick to hear my ur - gent

pray. May all who seek to take my
- cord. May those who love your sav - ing
plea. You are my help, my Sav - iour

life be put to shame with - out de - lay.
power say ev - er - more, 'Ex - alt the Lord!'
God! Do not de - lay; re - mem - ber me.

Words: © 1987 CRC Publications,
2850 Kalamazoo SE, Grand Rapids, Michigan 49560, USA

From time beyond my memory

Passons 8 8 8 8 (LM)

Words: from Psalm 71
Michael Perry
Music: Keith Landis
arranged Jack Noble White

UNISON

1 From time be - yond my me - mo - ry your
2 But when the years are pass - ing by as
3 We praise you, God, the ho - ly One, pro -
4 Sing glo - ry to the Fa - ther, Son — and

love has been my rock, O Lord; since child-hood days I
friends de - part and spi - rits fail: O God, come quick - ly
- claim your love from day to day; ex - alt your tri - umphs
to the Spi - rit glo - ry be; let psalms to God on

trust - ed you, and in my youth de - clared your word.
to my side, that in your strength I may pre - vail.
to the skies and trust your mer - cy, come what may:
earth be - gun re - sound through all e - ter - ni - ty!

Alternative tunes: Eisenach, *Hymns for Today's Church* 64, O Tannenbaum, *Songs from the Psalms* 71A

Music: © Praise Publications

117

Words: © Michael Perry/Jubilate Hymns †

To those who rule our land

Maiden Way   6 6 8 8 6

Words: from Psalm 72
Michael Perry
Music: E Routley (1917–1982)

UNISON

1 To those who rule our

land, give jus-tice, love and truth; so help them to de-

-fend the poor, to keep us safe, to guard the law, and pros-per at your hand: 2 Let mer - cy all their days fall

as re - fresh - ing showers; so guide the peo - ple with your light that

we may flour - ish in your sight, and earth be filled with praise!

Surely God the Lord is good

Calon Lân 7 7 7 7 D

Words: from Psalm 73
Michael Perry
Music: J Hughes (1873–1932)
arranged John Barnard

1 Sure-ly God the Lord is good,___ guid-ing all whose hearts are
2 When my stum-bling foot-steps tire,___ strength-en me in all I
3 Yes, this earth-bound fan-ta-sy___ shall dis-perse when you a-

pure;___ at God's hands we take our food,___ in God's love we are se-
do___ earth has no more I de-sire;___ whom have I in heaven but
-rise;___ when you come to wel-come me___ to your home be-yond the

-cure:___ vain-ly do the heath-en cry,___ 'Can the Most High watch us
you?___ Though my flesh and heart shall fail,___ you sup-ply___ im-mor-tal
skies.___ Glo-ry be to God to-day,___ ev-ery heart by grace for-

all?' Shamed by that all-see-ing eye___ soon the boast-ing proud will fall.
needs; with your help___ I shall pre-vail___ and pro-claim your per-fect deeds.
-given; souls re-deemed and an-gels say,___ Glo-ry in the high-est heaven!

Alternative tune: Hollingside, *Hymns for Today's Church* 438

O God, we thank you

Cople 8 8 8 8 (LM)

Words: from Psalm 75
Michael Perry
Music: Paul Edwards

1 O God, we thank you that your name is known and
feared through all the earth; your sen-tence waits the ap-point-ed time and thun-der brings your judge-ments forth.

2 The proud you cau-tion not to boast, the wick-ed,
not to raise their eyes; for you are king from east to west, and you a-lone shall have the praise!

3 We come be-fore you, God of gods — your power shall
cut the wick-ed down; we wor-ship you as Lord of lords — you lift us up to share your throne!

Alternative tune: Winchester New, *Hymns for Today's Church* 112

Music: © Paul Edwards/Jubilate Hymns †   Words: © Michael Perry/Jubilate Hymns †

76(i) Silent the earth when God arose

St Bartholomew's Pico Rivera   8 6 8 6 (CM)

Words: from Psalm 76
David Mowbray
Music: Keith Landis
arranged Betty Pulkingham

UNISON

1 Si - lent the earth___ when___ God___ a - rose
2 So let earth's ty - rants___ gaze___ in fear,
3 Let God be praised, Je - ru - sa - lem,

in jus - tice for the meek,   when all the strong were
as e - vil - do - ers should,   to see their wick - ed
and known through-out the earth: now is the mo - ment,

cast a - side   and mer - cy spared the weak.
deeds trans - formed to pro - vi - den - tial good.
now the time   to tell God's sov - ereign worth!

Silent the earth when God arose

Plumstead 8 6 8 6 (CM)

Words: from Psalm 76
David Mowbray
Music: John Joubert
commissioned for *The Cambridge Hymnal*

1 Si - lent the earth when God a - rose
2 So let earth's ty - rants gaze in fear,
3 Let God be praised, Je - ru - sa - lem,

in jus - tice for the meek,_____ when all the strong were
as e - vil - do - ers should,_____ to see their wick - ed
and known through-out the earth:_____ now is the mo - ment,

cast a - side and mer - cy spared_ the weak.
deeds trans-formed to pro - vi - den - tial good.
now the time to tell_ God's sov - ereign worth!

Alternative tune: Richmond, *Hymns for Today's Church* 541

77   I cried out for heaven to hear me

Now join we   9 8 9 8

Words: from Psalm 77
Michael Perry
Music: Michael Metcalf

UNISON

1 I cried out for hea - ven to hear me,
2 But in my des - pair I re - mem - bered
3 You spoke in the wind and the thun - der,
4 Then thank you, O God, for your me - rit,

I reached out in sor - row for help;   no   coun - sel or
the songs of a long time a - go,   and   dreamed of the
the earth and the e - le - ments shook;   your   power tore the
your faith - ful - ness al - ways the same;   the   Fa - ther, the

com - fort would cheer me,   my spi - rit a - ban - doned all hope.
ma - jes - ty splen-doured   of God the al - migh - ty, the true:
wa - ters a - sun - der,   as Shep - herd, you guid - ed your flock.
Son and the Spi - rit –   one Lord o - ver all. Praise your name!

Music: © Stainer & Bell Ltd,
82 High Road, London N2 9PW
(USA) Galaxy Music Corporation,
131 West 86th Street, New York NY 10024

Words: © Michael Perry/Jubilate Hymns †

We will tell each generation

Restoration 8 7 8 7

Words: from Psalm 78
Michael Perry
Music: *The Southern Harmony* 1835
arranged John Barnard

1 We will tell each___ ge - ne - ra - tion
2 Tell the times of___ our re - bel - ling –
3 Tell how once, when___ spite and ter - ror
4 Tell the grace that___ falls from hea - ven,

all that you, our___ God, have done; how you called and
how we wan - dered___ from your way, how your law___ our
threat - ened to en - gulf our land, you de - fend - ed
an - gels' food as___ faith's re - ward; tell how sins___ may

led our___ na - tion, chose us out___ to be your own:
love com - pel - ling taught us hum - bly to o - bey:
us with___ vi - gour, saved us by___ a migh - ty hand.
be for - giv - en through the mer - cy of the Lord.

Alternative tune: Stuttgart, *Hymns for Today's Church* 8

80(i) God of hosts, you chose a vine

Catherine 7 7 7 7

Words: from Psalm 80
David Mowbray
Music: Richard Connolly

1 God of hosts, you chose a vine meant to___ bear the
2 Like a ce - dar, it grew strong — deep its___ roots, its
3 Des - o - late, to God we cry: 'Spare us___ from the
4 Turn us too, for we have failed, faith - ful - ness has

fin - est___ wine,___ set it in a pro - mised
ten - drils___ long;___ yet, in en - vy those a -
e - ne - my!'___ God of hosts, turn back a -
not___ pre - vailed;___ vi - sit, Lord, and heal your

vv 1-3   v 4

land,___ nur - tured by your care - ful hand:___
- round___ stripped its branch - es to___ the ground.___
- gain,___ all such wick - ed - ness re - strain:___
vine,___ on its fruit let glo - ry shine!

God of hosts, you chose a vine 80(ii)

St Bees   7 7 7 7

Words: from Psalm 80
David Mowbray
Music: J B Dykes (1823–1876)

1 God of hosts, you chose a vine meant to
2 Like a ce - dar, it grew strong — deep its
3 Des - o - late, to God we cry: 'Spare us
4 Turn us too, for we have failed, faith - ful -

bear the fin - est wine, set it in a pro - mised
roots, its ten - drils long; yet, in en - vy those a -
from the e - ne - my!' God of hosts, turn back a -
- ness has not pre - vailed; vi - sit, Lord, and heal your

land, nur - tured by your___ care - ful hand:
- round stripped its branch - es___ to the ground.
- gain, all such wick - ed - ness re - strain:
vine, on its fruit let___ glo - ry shine!

81 Sing merrily to God

Speen 6 6 8 6 (SM)

Words: from Psalm 81
David Mowbray
Music: Anthony Greening

1 Sing merrily to God whose
2 Remember Israel's plight in
3 Remember too their pride, their

arm has done great things, and play with all the
Egypt's far-off land: how God, unaided,
murmurings on the way; recall how they for-

skill you have on trumpet, pipe and strings.
rescued them with strong and outstretched hand.
-sook the Lord and chose to disobey.

4 Let us not act like them,
but walk in faith again
and claim the gifts that God will shower
refreshing as the rain.

5 Sing merrily to God,
the Shepherd of his flock
who feeds his people, as of old,
with honey from the rock.

Alternative tune: Narenza, *Psalms for Today* 163B, *Hymns for Today's Church* 568

God is king – be warned, you mighty

82

Llanymawddwy 8 7 8 7 D

Words: from Psalm 82
Michael Perry
Music: David Preston

1 God is king – be warned, you_ migh-ty; God is judge through all the land:
2 There are lands that have no_ hon-our, hear no wis-dom, see no light;

or - der your af - fairs with jus - tice, rule with firm but_ gen - tle_ hand.
blind, they stum-ble in the_ dark-ness, lea - der - less, they shake with fright.

Help the weak, sup - port the_ need - y, take to heart the fa - ther - less;
Trem-ble, all you migh-ty_ rul - ers; ev - ery na - tion, know God's worth:

prove the rights of those who_ suf - fer, meet the poor in their dis - tress.
power and wealth are God's pos - sess - ion, who a - lone shall judge the_ earth!

Alternative tune: Gott Will's machen, *Psalms for Today* 100A(ii), *Hymns for Today's Church* 360

84A How lovely is your dwelling-place

Melchbourne 8 4 8 8 4

Words: from Psalm 84
Barbara Woollett
Music: Paul Edwards

1 How love - ly is your dwell - ing-place, O Lord___ most
2 The spar - row comes to build her nest, O Lord___ most
3 Your peo - ple come to you a - gain, O Lord___ most

high,_____ we long to know more of your grace, and
high,_____ and in your house finds peace and rest: so
high,_____ for here we feel your strength, like rain re -

yearn to see you face to face, O Lord___ most high!
may we too be ev - er blessed, O Lord___ most high!
-fresh - ing us through toil and pain, O Lord___ most high!

4 In fellowship your love we share,
    O Lord most high;
  far better is one day of prayer
  than any spent in worldly care,
    O Lord most high!

5 How lovely is your dwelling-place,
    O Lord most high;
  we bring you all our trust and praise,
  and ask your blessing on our days,
    O Lord most high!

O Lord, the mansions where you dwell   84B

QEGS 8 8 8 8 (LM)

Words: from Psalm 84
Paul Wigmore
Music: Gareth D Green

1 O Lord, the mansions where you dwell are overflowing with your love; while here on earth my soul knows well of lasting joy in heaven above.

2 And, Lord, my heart and flesh cry out in longing for that holy place; an end to sorrow, sin and doubt, the revelation of your face.

3 One day within your courts, O Lord, one day set free from every fear, one day with your dear name adored is better than a thousand here.

4 For those, O Lord, who trust in you: direct their eyes to see your ways, their heart to love, their hands to do, their head to bow, their lips to praise.

Alternative tune: St Laurence, *Hymns for Today's Church* 512

How lovely is your dwelling-place

Words: Psalm 84
from *The Liturgical Psalter*
David Frost and others
Music: C H H Parry (1848–1918)

1 **How lovely ' is your ' dwelling-place:**
 O ' Lord ' God of ' hosts!
2 My soul has a desire and longing to enter the ' courts · of the ' Lord:
 my heart and my flesh re'joice · in the ' living ' God.

3 The sparrow has found her a home
 and the swallow a nest where she may ' lay her ' young:
 even your altar O Lord of ' hosts ' my ' King · and my ' God.
4 Blessed are those who ' dwell in · your ' house:
 they will ' always · be ' praising ' you.

5 Blessed are those whose ' strength · is in ' you:
 in whose ' heart · are the ' highways · to ' Zion;
6 who going through the valley of dryness
 find there a spring from ' which to ' drink:
 till the autumn ' rain shall ' clothe it · with ' blessings.

Second part
7 They go from ' strength to ' strength:
 they appear every one of them before the ' God of ' gods in ' Zion.

8 O Lord God of hosts ' hear my ' prayer:
 give ' ear O ' God of ' Jacob.
9 Behold O God ' him who · reigns ' over us:
 and look upon the ' face of ' your a'nointed.

10 One day in your courts is ' better · than a ' thousand:
 I would rather stand at the threshold of the house of my God
 than ' dwell · in the ' tents of · un'godliness.
11 For the Lord God is a rampart and a shield
 the Lord gives ' favour · and ' honour:
 and no good thing will he withhold from ' those who ' walk in ' innocence.

Second part
12 O Lord ' God of ' hosts:
 blessed are those who ' put their ' trust in ' you.

 Glory to the Father and ' to the ' Son:
 and ' to the ' Holy ' Spirit;
 as it was in the be'ginning · is ' now:
 and shall be for ' ever. ' A'men.

When this land knew

Great Oxendon   10 10 10 10

Words: from Psalm 85
Christopher Idle
Music: Paul Edwards

UNISON

1 When this land knew God's gra-cious love out-poured guilt was re-
2 But now where wrong so fla-grant-ly has trod will you for-
3 O let me hear God's word of sweet com-mand: peace to his
4 That day draws near when truth will join with grace, jus-tice and

-moved and cap-tive lives re-stored; then was drawn back the
ev - er pun-ish with your rod? Once more re-vive us!
saints, sal - va-tion is at hand; peace to his peo - ple,
peace will meet in love's em-brace; faith on the earth, and

an - ger of the Lord, his peo - ple par - doned, their sins___ for-giv-en.
Give us life, O God! Give joy for an - guish; for wrath,___ sal - va-tion.
glo - ry in our land for those who fear him, who turn___ and wor-ship.
from his ho-ly place he comes in glo - ry, the right - eous Sav-iour.

Alternative tune: Sine Nomine, *Hymns for Today's Church* 567

86A(i)

Hear me, O Lord

Pamela 10 8 10 8

Words: from Psalm 86
Michael Perry
Music: Gareth D Green

UNISON

1 Hear me, O Lord, and re - spond to my prayer,
2 Bring me your joy as I wor - ship you, Lord,
3 Give me a sign of your good - ness, O Lord,

guard well my life, for I love you:
come to my heart, for I need you;
grant me the strength that o - beys you:

no - thing com - pares with the won - ders you do,___
teach me your way, let me walk in your truth ___
you are com - pas - sion, a - bound - ing in love, ___

vv 1 and 2 | v 3

for there is no ___ god a - bove you.
I can-not fail when I heed you.
you are my king, and I praise you.

OPTIONAL DESCANT for verse 3. (Instrumental or vocal sung to 'Ah')

Hear me, O Lord

Thursford Green 10 8 10 8

Words: from Psalm 86
Michael Perry
Music: Derek Williams

UNISON

1 Hear me, O Lord, and re-spond to my prayer,
2 Bring me your joy as I wor-ship you, Lord,
3 Give me a sign of your good-ness, O Lord,

guard well my life, for I love you: no-thing com-pares with the
come to my heart, for I need you;   teach me your way, let me
grant me the strength that o-beys you: you are com-pas-sion, a-

won-ders you do,   for there is no god a-bove you.
walk in your truth –   I can-not fail when I heed you.
-bound-ing in love,   you are my king, and I praise you.

For all your boundless gifts

87(i)

Ridley 6 6 8 6 (SM)

Words: from Psalm 87
David Mowbray
Music: Christopher Blissard-Barnes
arranged John Barnard

1 For all your bound - less gifts____ we
2 So was Je - ru - sa - lem____ both
3 Through all our ci - ties, Lord,____ let
4 So trum - pet - ers shall sound____ and

of - fer,____ Lord, our praise;____ for pla - ces which have
Is - rael's_ joy and pride,____ the ci - ty of the
streams of____ jus - tice flow;____ there may_ the king - dom
earth and__ hea - ven ring;____ then shall__ the peo - ple

shel - tered us and__ shaped our earth - ly days.
Lord__ most high where_ kings_ were born and died.
of____ your Christ - a____ spread - ing ce - dar_ grow.
say__ A - men and__ songs_ of glad - ness sing!

87(ii) For all your boundless gifts

St Ethelwald   6 6 8 6 (SM)

Words: from Psalm 87
David Mowbray
Music: W H Monk (1823–1889)

1 For all___ your bound - less___ gifts we
2 So was___ Je - ru - sa - lem both
3 Through all___ our ci - ties,___ Lord, let
4 So trum - pet - ers shall___ sound and

of - fer,___ Lord, our praise; for plac - es which have___
Is - rael's___ joy and pride, the ci - ty of the___
streams of___ jus - tice flow; there may the king - dom___
earth and___ hea - ven ring; then shall the peo - ple___

shel - tered___ us and shaped our___ earth - ly___ days.
Lord___ most___ high where kings___ were___ born___ and___ died.
of___ your___ Christ - a spread - ing___ ce - dar___ grow.
say___ A - men and songs___ of___ glad - ness___ sing!

Alternative tune: Dominica, *Hymns for Today's Church* 380

O Lord, the God who saves me

88

Blunham 7 6 7 6

Words: from Psalm 88
Michael Perry
Music: Paul Edwards

1 O Lord, the God who saves me, to
2 Your an - ger lies up - on me, I
3 And shall the dead sing prais - es, and

you my spi - rit cries; my world is full of
can - not make a - mends; your waves, they o - ver -
can the dark - ness see your right - eous ways, your

trou - ble, and hope of mer - cy dies.
- whelm me, you take a - way my friends. grave!
won - ders, your faith - ful - ness to me?

4 I call to you in waking,
and seek you all day long:
O hear me, Lord and Saviour –
restore to me my song.

5 My God shall yet uplift me,
the Spirit come to save,
and Jesus my redeemer
shall tear me from the grave!

Alternative tune: Christus der ist mein Leben, *Psalms for Today* 27A

89A(i) Timeless love

Patrixbourne 8 7 8 7 7 7

Words: from Psalm 89
Timothy Dudley-Smith
Music: John Barnard

1 Time-less love! We sing the sto - ry, praise his won - ders, tell his worth; love more fair than hea-ven's glo - ry, love more firm than an-cient earth! Tell his faith - ful-ness a - broad: who is like him? Praise the Lord!

The Harmony version is compatible with the Unison setting.

Timeless love

Timeless love 8 7 8 7 7 7

Words: from Psalm 89
Timothy Dudley-Smith
Music: Norman Warren

1 Time-less love! We sing the sto - ry, praise his won - ders, tell his
2 By his faith - ful-ness sur - round-ed, north and south his hand pro -
3 Truth and right - eous-ness en - throne him, just and e - qual are his

worth; love more fair than hea-ven's glo - ry, love more
- claim; earth and hea - ven formed and found - ed, skies and
ways; more than hap - py, those who own him, more than

firm than an - cient earth! Tell his faith - ful - ness a -
seas, de - clare his name! Wind and storm o - bey his
joy, their songs of praise! Sun and shield and great re -

- broad: who is like him? Praise the Lord!
word:
- ward:

Alternative tune: All Saints, *Hymns for Today's Church* 215

Our God eternal, reigning

90A

Innsbruck 7 7 6 7 7 8

Words: from Psalm 90
Timothy Dudley-Smith
Music: German traditional melody

1 Our God eternal, reigning, creation's life sustaining, our refuge and our home; enthroned, in light surrounded, when earth was yet unfounded, the living God, to him we come.

2 We fade, a dream that passes, like withered meadow grasses when summer's sun has shone. Before that face all-seeing of God who gave us being we pass away and we are gone.

3 O God of mercy, hear us, in steadfast love draw near us, from age to age the same; that we, by grace defended, when earthly days are ended may live to praise a Saviour's name.

143

90B God everlasting, at your word

Orphan Girl 8 6 8 6 (CM)

Words: from Psalm 90
David Mowbray
Music: *Sacred Harp* 1902
arranged David Iliff

1 God ev - er - last - ing, at your word the
2 Our days like dreams come to an end, our
3 Teach us, good Lord, to count our days, to
4 Lord, at your hand we have re - ceived the

hills in splen - dour rise; they o - ver - sha - dow
sto - ry soon is told when strength is spent, and
che - rish ev - ery hour; to seek your will, to
cup of joy and pain: pour out the ful - ness

hu - man life whose glo - ry swift - ly dies.
beau - ty fades, and bo - dies have grown old.
do your work, and trust your migh - ty power.
of your grace and we shall sing a - gain!

Alternative tune: London New, *Hymns for Today's Church* 332

Safe in the shadow of the Lord

Creator God 8 6 8 6 (CM)

Words: from Psalm 91
Timothy Dudley-Smith
Music: Norman Warren

WOMEN
4 His holy angels keep my feet
secure from every stone;
   I trust in him,
   I trust in him,
and unafraid go on.

ALL
5 Strong in the everlasting name,
and in my Father's care,
   I trust in him,
   I trust in him,
who hears and answers prayer.

6 Safe in the shadow of the Lord,
possessed by love divine,
   I trust in him,
   I trust in him,
and meet his love with mine.

Safe in the shadow of the Lord

Stanton 8 6 8 6 (CM)

Words: from Psalm 91
Timothy Dudley-Smith
Music: John Barnard

UNISON

1 Safe in the sha - dow of the Lord, be - neath his
2 My hope is set on God a - lone though Sa - tan
MEN 3 From fears and phan - toms of the night, from foes a -

hand__ and power,
spreads his snare; I trust in him, I trust in
-bout__ my way,

him, my for - tress and__ my tower.
to keep me in__ his care.
by dark - ness as__ by day.

WOMEN
4 His holy angels keep my feet
   secure from every stone;
     I trust in him,
     I trust in him,
   and unafraid go on.

ALL
5 Strong in the everlasting name,
   and in my Father's care,
     I trust in him,
     I trust in him,
   who hears and answers prayer.

6 Safe in the shadow of the Lord,
   possessed by love divine,
     I trust in him,
     I trust in him,
   and meet his love with mine.

Make music to the Lord

Rodmell 8 6 8 6 (CM)

Words: from Psalm 92
Christopher Idle
Music: English traditional melody
arranged David Iliff

1 Make mu - sic to the Lord__ most__ high whose__
2 Lord, when we see all you__ have__ done our__
WOMEN 3 The god - less mind will ne - ver__ know – be -

praise is__ our__ de - light: we__ sing your__ love__ as__
songs of__ joy re - sound: your__ hand - i - work, how__
- cause its__ sense__ is__ void – that__ though the__ wick - ed__

day__ be - gins, your__ faith - ful - ness__ by__ night.
vast__ it__ is, your__ coun - sels, how__ pro - found!
spread like__ grass, they__ all shall be__ de - stroyed.

ALL
4 For ever, Lord, you are supreme;
   your throne remains on high
   while rebels meet eternal doom
   and evil-doers die.

MEN
5 But like the cedar and the palm
   the righteous stand serene;
   they flourish in the house of God,
   their leaves are fresh and green.

ALL
6 To fruitful age they still proclaim
   the Lord who makes them new –
   our God, in whom no wrong is found,
   my Rock, for ever true.

Make music to the Lord

Bishopthorpe 8 6 8 6 (CM)

Words: from Psalm 92
Christopher Idle
Music: J Clarke (c1674–1707)

1 Make mu - sic to the Lord most high whose
2 Lord, when we see all you have done our
WOMEN 3 The god - less mind will ne - ver know = be -

praise is our de - light: we sing your love as
songs of joy re - sound: your hand - i - work, how
- cause its sense is void = that though the wick - ed

day be - gins, your faith - ful - ness by night.
vast it is, your coun - sels, how pro - found!
spread like grass, they all shall be des - troyed.

ALL
4 For ever, Lord, you are supreme;
your throne remains on high
while rebels meet eternal doom
and evil-doers die.

MEN
5 But like the cedar and the palm
the righteous stand serene;
they flourish in the house of God,
their leaves are fresh and green.

ALL
6 To fruitful age they still proclaim
the Lord who makes them new –
our God, in whom no wrong is found,
my Rock, for ever true.

Clothed in kingly majesty

Kingly majesty 7 5 5

Words: from Psalm 93
Michael Saward
Music: Norman Warren
Harmony: John Barnard

UNISON

1 Clothed in king-ly ma-jes-ty, robed in re-gal

power,_____ God is o-ver all.

HARMONY

2 Lord of all, un-shake-a-ble,_____ throned be-yond all
3 Great-er than the ri-ver's roar_____ and the surg-ing
4 Change-less as his law's de-crees,_____ crowned our ho-ly

time,_____ God is o-ver all._____
sea,_____
king,_____

The Harmony and Unison versions are not harmonically compatible.

God is King! The Lord is reigning

Crail 8 7 8 8 8 7 7 7

Words: from Psalm 93
Timothy Dudley-Smith
Music: Peter Cutts

UNISON

1 God is King! The Lord is reign-ing, might and ma-jes-ty his robe;

to his seat on high as-cend-ed, gird-ed round with glo-ry splen-did,

there in time and space sus-tain-ing this our star-en-cir-cled globe.

Fore-or-dained and found-ed fast, ev-er-more his throne shall last!

The Harmony version is not harmonically compatible with the Unison setting.
Only one of the two interlined verses should be sung in harmony.

95A   Come with all joy to sing to God

Fulda 8 8 8 8 (LM)

Words: from Psalm 95, *Venite*
Christopher Idle
Music: W Gardiner *Sacred Melodies* 1815

1 Come with all joy to sing___ to God our sav - ing
2 In ho - li - ness and light___ ar - rayed a - bove all
WOMEN 3 The earth is his from east___ to west, from o - cean -

rock, the liv - ing Lord; in glad thanks - giv - ing
gods that we___ have made he is the one___ al -
- floor to moun - tain - crest; he made the seas___ and

seek his face___ with songs of vic - to - ry___ and grace.
- migh - ty king,___ and his the glo - ry that___ we sing.
formed the lands,___ he shaped the is - lands by___ his hands.

MEN
4 Come near to worship! come with faith,
bow down to him who gives us breath:
God is our shepherd, he alone;
we are his people, all his own.

WOMEN
5 But if you hear God's voice today
do not reject what he will say:
when Israel wandered from God's path
they suffered forty years of wrath.

MEN
6 That generation went astray,
they did not want to know his way;
they put their saviour to the test,
and saw his power, but lost their rest.

ALL
7 So to the God of earth and heaven,
the Father, Spirit, Son, be given
praise now, as praise has ever been
and ever shall be praise. Amen.

Come, worship God

Jesmian 11 10 11 10

95B(i)

Words: from Psalm 95, *Venite*
Michael Perry
Music: G Thalben-Ball (1896–1987)

1 Come, wor-ship God who is wor-thy of hon-our,
2 Ruled by his might are the heights of the moun-tains,
3 We are his peo-ple, the sheep of his pas-ture,
4 Now let us lis-ten, for God speaks a-mong us,

en-ter his pre-sence with thanks and a song!
held in his hands are the depths of the earth;
he is our ma-ker and to him we pray;
o-pen our hearts and re-ceive what he says:

He is the rock of his peo-ple's sal-va-tion,
his is the sea, his the land, for he made them,
glad-ly we kneel in o-be-dience be-fore him
peace be to all who re-mem-ber his good-ness,

to whom our ju-bi-lant prais-es be-long.
king a-bove all gods, who gave us our birth.
great is the God whom we wor-ship this day!
trust in his word and re-joice in his ways!

95B(ii)   Come, worship God

Epiphany Hymn   11 10 11 10

Words: from Psalm 95, *Venite*
Michael Perry
Music: J F Thrupp (1827–1867)

1 Come, wor-ship God who is wor-thy of hon-our,
en-ter his pre-sence with thanks and a song!
He is the rock of his peo-ple's sal-va-tion,
to whom our ju-bi-lant prais-es be-long.

2 Ruled by his might are the heights of the moun-tains,
held in his hands are the depths of the earth;
his is the sea, his the land, for he made them,
king a-bove all gods, who gave us our birth.

3 We are his peo-ple, the sheep of his pas-ture,
he is our ma-ker and to him we pray;
glad-ly we kneel in o-be-dience be-fore him—
great is the God whom we wor-ship this day!

4 Now let us lis-ten, for God speaks a-mong us,
o-pen our hearts and re-ceive what he says:
peace be to all who re-mem-ber his good-ness,
trust in his word and re-joice in his ways!

Alternative tune: O quanta qualia, *Hymns for Today's Church* 18

O come, let us sing out to the Lord

95C

Words: Psalm 95
from *The Liturgical Psalter*
David Frost and others

C V Stanford (1852–1924)

H Lawes (1595–1662)

1 O come, let us sing ˈ out · to the ˈ Lord:
   let us shout in triumph to the ˈ rock of ˈ our salˈvation.
2 Let us come before his ˈ face with ˈ thanksgiving:
   and cry ˈ out to · him ˈ joyfully · in ˈ psalms.

3 For the Lord is a ˈ great ˈ God:
   and a great ˈ king a·bove ˈ all ˈ gods.
4 In his hand are the ˈ depths · of the ˈ earth:
   and the peaks of the ˈ mountains · are ˈ his ˈ also.

Second part
5 The sea is his and ˈ he ˈ made it:
   his hands ˈ moulded ˈ dry ˈ land.

6 Come let us worship and ˈ bow ˈ down:
   and kneel beˈfore the ˈ Lord our ˈ maker.
7 For he is the ˈ Lord our ˈ God:
   we are his ˈ people · and the ˈ sheep of · his ˈ pasture.

8 Today if only you would hear his voice
   'Do not harden your ˈ hearts · as at ˈ Meribah:
   as on that day at ˈ Massah ˈ in the ˈ wilderness;
9 when your ˈ fathers ˈ tested me:
   put me to proof though ˈ they had ˈ seen my ˈ works.

10 'Forty years long I loathed that generˈation · and ˈ said:
   "It is a people who err in their hearts,
   for they ˈ do not ˈ know my ˈ ways";
11 of whom I ˈ swore · in my ˈ wrath:
   "They ˈ shall not ˈ enter · my ˈ rest."'

   Glory to the Father and ˈ to the ˈ Son:
   and ˈ to the ˈ Holy ˈ Spirit;
   as it was in the beˈginning · is ˈ now:
   and shall be for ˈ ever. ˈ Aˈmen.

See also *Venite*, (ASB 1980), *Psalms for Today* 151

96A Sing a new song of glory

Lord of the years   11 10 11 10

Words: from Psalm 96
Stephen Horsfall
Music: Michael Baughen
arranged David Iliff
Descant: John Barnard

1 Sing a new song of glo-ry and sal-va-tion,
through all the earth let voi-ces now be raised;
speak of God's migh-ty power in ev-ery na-tion —
great is the Lord, and great-ly to be praised!

2 Sing and a-dore, shout loud with ju-bi-la-tion,
tell of the truth and splen-dour of that Name;
come with thanks-giv-ing, wor-ship, all cre-a-tion —
praise be to God for ev-er-more the same.

Organ

Alternative tune: Strength and stay, *Hymns for Today's Church* 300

earth   are   blend - ing   as   all   cre -

earth   and   hea - ven   blend - ing   as   all   cre -

- a - tion_____   joins   to   sing   God's   grace!

- a - tion   joins   to   sing   God's   grace!

O sing to the Lord a new song

Words: from Psalm 96
from *The Liturgical Psalter*
David Frost and others
Music: John Barnard

96B

Music: © John Barnard/Jubilate Hymns †

bless his ho - ly name: pro - claim the good news of his sal -

- va - tion from day to day. Declare his

glo - ry a-mong the na - tions: and his won - ders a - mong all

peo-ples. ALL O sing to the Lord a new song:

Organ   Man.   Ped.

160

sing to the Lord_ all the earth. _ CHOIR 2 As for all the gods of the na -

- tions they_ are mere i - dols:_ it is the Lord who made_____ the

heavens. Ma - jes - ty_____ and glo - ry are_ be - fore him:

beau - ty_ and power are in_____ his sanc - tu - ary._ ALL O

Organ

161

sing to the Lord a new song: sing to the Lord all the

Man. Ped.

earth._ CHOIR 3 O wor-ship the Lord_ in the beau - ty of_____ his

ho - li - ness:_ let the whole earth stand_____ in awe of him._

Say a-mong the na-tions that the Lord_____ is king: he shall judge the world with right-eous-ness___ and the peo-ples with___ his

truth.

f

ALL O sing to the Lord a new song:

Organ

Man.

Ped.

sing to the Lord all the earth. O sing to the Lord a new song:

Man.

Ped.

sing to the Lord all the earth.

ff

CHOIR O sing a new song!

ff

163

97 The everlasting Lord is king

Neville Court 8 6 8 6 (CM)

Words: from Psalm 97
Timothy Dudley-Smith
Music: Derek Williams

1 The ev - er - last - ing___ Lord is king — let
2 He comes in clouds with___ fire and flame to
3 The sun and moon and___ star - ry sky his
4 De - fend - ed by his___ hand di - vine his

o - cean find a voice,___ her fur - thest shores his
make his judge-ments known;___ the moun - tains trem - ble
glo - ries blaze a - broad,___ the one e - ter - nal
saints se - cure re - main;___ for them the light of

tri - umph sing and___ all the earth re - joice.
at his name and___ melt be - fore his throne.
God most high, the___ true and liv - ing Lord.
life shall shine, the___ King of love shall reign.

Alternative tune: Kilmarnock, *Hymns for Today's Church* 448

Sing to God new songs of worship

Ode to Joy 8 7 8 7 D

Words: from Psalm 98, *Cantate Domino*
Michael Baughen
Music: L van Beethoven (1770–1827)

1 Sing to God new songs of wor-ship— all his deeds are mar-vel-lous;
2 Sing to God new songs of wor-ship— earth has seen his vic-to-ry;
3 Sing to God new songs of wor-ship— let the sea now make a noise;

he has brought sal-va-tion to us with his hand and ho-ly arm.
let the lands of earth be joy-ful prais-ing him with thank-ful-ness.
all on earth and in the wa-ters, sound your prais-es to the Lord.

He has shown to all the— na-tions right-eous-ness and sav-ing power;
Sound up-on the harp his— prais-es, play to— him with me-lo-dy;—
Let the hills re-joice to-ge-ther, let the— ri-vers clap their hands,

he re-called his truth and— mer-cy to his peo-ple Is-ra-el.
let the trum-pets sound his— tri-umph, show your joy to God the king!
for with right-eous-ness and— jus-tice he will come to judge the earth.

This may be sung in G♭.

Sing a new song to the Lord

Onslow Square 7 7 11 8

Words: from Psalm 98, *Cantate Domino*
Timothy Dudley-Smith
Music: David Wilson

1 Sing a new song to the Lord, he to whom won-ders be -
2 Now to the ends of the earth see his sal - va - tion is
3 Sing a new song and re - joice, pub - lish his prais - es a -
4 Join with the hills and the sea thun - ders of praise to pro -

- long! Re - joice in his tri - umph and
shown: and still he re - mem - bers his
- broad! Let voi - ces in cho - rus with
- long! In judge - ment and jus - tice he

tell of his power = O sing to the
mer - cy and truth, un - chang - ing in
trum - pet and horn, re - sound for the
comes to the earth = O sing to the

vv 1-3   v 4

Lord a new song!
love to his own.
joy of the Lord!
Lord a new song!

Sing a new song to the Lord

98B(ii)

Littlebourne 7 7 11 8

Words: from Psalm 98, *Cantate Domino*
Timothy Dudley-Smith
Music: John Barnard

1 Sing a new song to the Lord, he to whom won-ders be - long! Re - joice in his tri-umph and tell of his power – O sing to the Lord a new song!

2 Now to the ends of the earth see his sal - va - tion is shown: and still he re-mem-bers his mer - cy and truth, un - chang-ing in love to his own.

3 Sing a new song and re - joice, pub - lish his prais-es a - broad! Let voi - ces in cho - rus, with trum - pet and horn, re - sound for the joy of the Lord!

4 Join with the hills and the sea thun - ders of praise to pro-long! In judge-ment and jus - tice he comes to the earth – O sing a new song!

98c   O sing to the Lord a new song

Words: Psalm 98, *Cantate Domino*
from *The Liturgical Psalter*
David Frost and others
Music: J Goss (1800–1880)

1   O sing to the Lord a ⏐ new ⏐ song:
     for he has ⏐ done ⏐ marvel·lous ⏐ things;
2   his right hand and his ⏐ holy ⏐ arm:
     they have ⏐ got ⏐ him the ⏐ victory.

3   The Lord has made ⏐ known · his sal⏐vation:
     he has revealed his just de⏐liverance · in the ⏐ sight of · the ⏐ nations.
4   He has remembered his mercy and faithfulness towards the ⏐ house of ⏐ Israel:
     and all the ends of the earth have seen the sal⏐vation ⏐ of our ⏐ God.

5   Shout with joy to the Lord ⏐ all the ⏐ earth:
     break into ⏐ singing · and ⏐ make ⏐ melody.
6   Make melody to the Lord up⏐on the ⏐ harp:
     upon the harp and ⏐ with the ⏐ sounds of ⏐ praise.

7   With trumpets ⏐ and with ⏐ horns:
     cry out in triumph be⏐fore the ⏐ Lord the ⏐ king.
8   Let the sea roar and ⏐ all that ⏐ fills it:
     the good earth and ⏐ those who ⏐ live up⏐on it.

9   Let the rivers ⏐ clap their ⏐ hands:
     and let the mountains ring out to⏐gether · be⏐fore the ⏐ Lord;
10   for he comes to ⏐ judge the ⏐ earth:
     he shall judge the world with righteousness
     and the ⏐ peoples ⏐ with ⏐ equity.

     Glory to the Father and ⏐ to the ⏐ Son:
     and ⏐ to the ⏐ Holy ⏐ Spirit;
     as it was in the be⏐ginning · is ⏐ now:
     and shall be for ⏐ ever. ⏐ A⏐men.

God is king – the nations tremble

Goodwyn's Vale 8 8 8 6

Words: from Psalm 99
Michael Saward
Music: Alan Horsey

UNISON

1 God is king – the na-tions trem - ble, he is
2 God is king – he calls for jus - tice, he pro-
3 God is king, yet all may know— him – priests and
4 God is king, yet he for - gives— us, bears our

throned – the earth is quak - ing;
-claims his right-eous judge - ment; Lord su-preme, the peo-ple
pro - phets heard his pre - cepts;
sins in his own bo - dy;

v 4 only

praise— him: Ho - ly, ho - ly, ho - ly!

v 4

100A(i)   Come, rejoice before your maker

Come rejoice   8 7 8 7

Words: from Psalm 100, *Jubilate Deo*
Michael Baughen
Music: Noël Tredinnick

1 Come, re - joice be - fore your ma - ker
2 Know for cer - tain that Je - ho - vah
3 Come with grate - ful hearts be - fore him,
4 For the Lord our God is gra - cious —

all you peo - ples of the earth; — serve the Lord your
is the true and on - ly God: — we are his, for
en - ter now his courts with praise; — show your thank - ful -
ev - er - last - ing in his love; — and to ev - ery

God with glad - ness, come be - fore him with a song!
he has made us; we are sheep with - in his fold.
- ness to - wards him, give due hon - our to his name.
ge - ne - ra - tion his great faith - ful - ness en - dures.

Come, rejoice before your maker   100A(ii)

Gott Will's machen   8 7 8 7

Words: from Psalm 100, *Jubilate Deo*
Michael Baughen
Music: J L Steiner (1668–1761)

1 Come, re-joice be-fore your ma-ker
2 Know for cer-tain that Je-ho-vah
3 Come with grate-ful hearts be-fore him,
4 For the Lord our God is gra-cious –

all you peo-ples of the earth; serve the Lord your
is the true and on-ly God: we are his, for
en-ter now his courts with praise; show your thank-ful-
ev-er-last-ing in his love; and to ev-ery

God with glad-ness, come be-fore him with a song!
he has made us; we are sheep with-in his fold.
-ness to-wards him, give due hon-our to his name.
ge-ne-ra-tion his great faith-ful-ness en-dures.

100B   Sing, all creation

Long Crendon   11 11 11 5

Words: from Psalm 100, *Jubilate Deo*
James Quinn SJ
Music: John Barnard

1 Sing, all cre - a - tion, sing to God in gladness, joy - ous - ly serve him, sing - ing hymns of hom - age; chant - ing his prais - es, come be - fore his pre - sence: praise the Al - migh - ty!

Alternative tune: Iste Confessor, *Hymns for Today's Church* 391

2 Know that our God is Lord of all the
3 En - ter his tem - ple, ring - ing out his
4 Great in his good - ness is the Lord we

a - ges;___ he___ is our ma - ker: we are all his
prais - es;___ sing___ in thanks - giv - ing as you come be -
wor - ship;___ stead - fast his kind - ness, love that knows no

crea - tures,___ peo - ple he fash - ioned, sheep he
- fore___ him;___ bless - ing his boun - ty, glo - ri -
end - ing;___ faith - ful his word is, change - less,

leads to pas - ture:___
- fy his great - ness:___ praise___ the Al - migh - ty!
ev - er - last - ing:___

The Harmony version is harmonically compatible with the Unison setting.

100c   O shout to the Lord in triumph

Words: Psalm 100, *Jubilate Deo*
from *The Liturgical Psalter*
David Frost and others

E Cutler (1831–1916)

T Norris (1741–1790)

1 O shout to the Lord in triumph ˈ all the ˈ earth:
   serve the Lord with gladness
   and come before his ˈ face with ˈ songs of ˈ joy.
2 Know that the Lord ˈ he is ˈ God:
   it is he who has made us and we are his;
   we are his ˈ people · and the ˈ sheep of · his ˈ pasture.

3 Come into his gates with thanksgiving
   and into his ˈ courts with ˈ praise:
   give thanks to him and ˈ bless his ˈ holy ˈ name.
4 For the Lord is good *
   his loving mercy ˈ is for ˈ ever:
   his faithfulness throughˈout all ˈ generˈations.

   Glory to the Father and ˈ to the ˈ Son:
   and ˈ to the ˈ Holy ˈ Spirit;
   as it was in the beˈginning is ˈ now:
   and shall be for ˈ ever. ˈ Aˈmen.

With joyful shouts acclaim the Lord · 100D

Tyrol 8 6 8 6 D (DCM)

Words: from Psalm 100, *Jubilate Deo*
David Preston
Music: Tyrolean melody
arranged David Iliff

1 With joy-ful shouts ac - claim the_ Lord, all peo - ple ev - ery - where;
3 As you ap-proach his tem - ple_ steps your thank-ful - ness pro - claim;

bow down to him in glad ac - cord, with songs of joy draw near!
come in with prais - es on your lips and bless his ho - ly name.

2 Ac - know-ledge God the Lord to be the one true God in - deed:
4 Re - joice be-cause the Lord is good, his stead - fast love is sure;

he made us all, his sheep are_ we, that in his pas-tures feed.
his faith-ful - ness has al - ways stood and shall for ev - er - more.

Alternative tune: Jackson, *Hymns for Today's Church* 572

101   With heart and hands washed clean

Webster   6 6 8 6 (SM)

Words: from Psalm 101
David Mowbray
Music: *Southern Harmony* 1835
arranged David Iliff

1 With heart and hands washed clean   I'll
2 For wick - ed - ness must pass like
3 Walk with me in God's house, all

sing your praise, O Lord— a song of mer - cy,
smoke, and drift a - way; de - ceit and pride shall
you of up - right heart: for those who keep his

yet a song of judge - ment and the sword:
be cast down like i - dols made of clay.
com - pa - ny no force can tear a - part.

Alternative tunes: Venice, *Psalms for Today* 133A(ii), *Hymns for Today's Church* 34,
Franconia, *Hymns for Today's Church* 110

You laid the foundations of earth 102A(i)

Limburg 8 8 8 8

Words: from Psalm 102
Michael Perry
Music: David Iliff

1 You laid the found - a - tions of earth,_____ the
2 Like cloth - ing the worlds shall be changed,_____ the
3 Your ser - vants shall trust in your love,_____ our

hea - vens were wrought by your hands;_____ they pe - rish, but you will re -
skies cast a - way like a veil;_____ but you, Lord, are al - ways the
child - ren shall walk in your ways,_____ till time holds us cap - tive no

- main,_____ they fal - ter, but your glo - ry stands._____
same,_____ your years like your words ne - ver fail._____
more_____ and pa - ra - dise rings with your praise!_____

102A(ii) You laid the foundations of earth

Grendon 8 8 8 8

Words: from Psalm 102
Michael Perry
Music: Paul Edwards

1 You laid the found-a-tions of earth, the
2 Like cloth-ing the worlds shall be changed, the
3 Your ser-vants shall trust in your love, our

hea-vens were wrought by your hands; they pe-rish, but you will re-
skies cast a-way like a veil; but you, Lord, are al-ways the
child-ren shall walk in your ways, till time holds us cap-tive no

-main, they fal-ter, but your glo-ry stands.
same, your years like your words ne-ver fail.
more and pa-ra-dise rings with your praise!

Praise the Lord and bless his name 103A

Mow Cop 7 7 7 7 7 7

Words: from Psalm 103
Timothy Dudley-Smith
Music: Brian Hoare

1 Praise the Lord and bless his name, life and peace in him are found.
2 High as heaven's furthest star, vaster than the shores of space,
3 Swifter than the winds that pass, fading as the summer flowers,
4 Praise the Lord of earth and heaven, angel hosts about his throne,

All his benefits proclaim, grace with love and mercy crowned:
so he bears our sins afar, so he brings to us his grace.
what though all our days are grass? faith and hope shall still be ours.
sinners by his grace forgiven, saints who his dominion own:

sins forgiven, strength restored! Sing my soul, and praise the Lord!
He who hears his children's prayer ever keeps us in his care.
God's unchanging love is sure and endures for evermore.
God of all, by all adored! Sing, my soul, and praise the Lord!

Alternative tune: England's Lane, *Hymns for Today's Church* 298

Praise the Lord O my soul

Words: Psalm 103
from *The Liturgical Psalter*
David Frost and others
Music: I Atkins (1869–1953)

1 Praise the Lord ' O my ' soul:
  and all that is within me ' praise his ' holy ' name.
2 Praise the Lord ' O my ' soul:
  and for'get not ' all his ' benefits,

3 who forgives ' all your ' sin:
  and ' heals ' all · your in'firmities,
4 who redeems your ' life · from the ' Pit:
  and crowns you with ' mercy ' and com'passion;

Second part
5 who satisfies your being with ' good ' things:
  so that your ' youth · is re'newed · like an ' eagle's.

6 The Lord ' works ' righteousness:
  and justice for ' all who ' are op'pressed.
7 He made known his ' ways to ' Moses:
  and his ' works · to the ' children · of ' Israel.

8 The Lord is full of com'passion · and ' mercy:
  slow to anger ' and of ' great ' goodness.
9 He will not ' always · be ' chiding:
  nor will he ' keep his ' anger · for ' ever.

10 He has not dealt with us ac'cording · to our ' sins:
  nor rewarded us ac'cording ' to our ' wickedness.
11 For as the heavens are high a'bove the ' earth:
  so great is his ' mercy · over ' those that ' fear him;

Music: © Novello & Co Ltd,
8/10 Lower James Street, London W1R 3PL

12   as far as the east is ˈ from the ˈ west:
     so far has he ˈ set our ˈ sins ˈ from us.
13   As a father is tender toˈwards his ˈ children:
     so is the Lord ˈ tender · to ˈ those that ˈ fear him.

Second part
14   For he knows of ˈ what · we are ˈ made:
     he reˈmembers · that we ˈ are but ˈ dust.

15   The days of man are ˈ but as ˈ grass:
     he flourishes ˈ like a ˈ flower · of the ˈ field;
16   when the wind goes over it ˈ it is ˈ gone:
     and its ˈ place will ˈ know it · no ˈ more.

17   But the merciful goodness of the Lord
     endures for ever and ever toward ˈ those that ˈ fear him:
     and his righteousness upˈon their ˈ children's ˈ children;
18   upon those who ˈ keep his ˈ covenant:
     and reˈmember · his comˈmandments · to ˈ do them.

19   The Lord has established his ˈ throne in ˈ heaven:
     and his ˈ kingdom ˈ rules · over ˈ all.
20   Praise the Lord all you his angels
     you that exˈcel in ˈ strength:
     you that fulfil his word
     and obey the ˈ voice of ˈ his comˈmandment.

21   Praise the Lord all ˈ you his ˈ hosts:
     his ˈ servants · who ˈ do his ˈ will.
22   Praise the Lord all his works
     in all places of ˈ his doˈminion:
     praise the ˈ Lord ˈ O my ˈ soul!

     Glory to the Father and ˈ to the ˈ Son:
     and ˈ to the ˈ Holy ˈ Spirit;
     as it was in the beˈginning · is ˈ now:
     and shall be for ˈ ever. ˈ Aˈmen.

103c The Lord is full of compassion

Words: from Psalm 103
from *The Liturgical Psalter*
David Frost and others
Music: Philip Moore

The Lord is full of com-pas-sion and mer-cy: slow to anger and of great good-ness.

He will not al-ways be chid-ing: nor will he keep his an-ger for ev-er.

He has not dealt with us ac-cord-ing to our sins:

nor rewarded us according to our wick - ed-ness. For as the heavens are

high a-bove the earth:_ so great is his mer-cy o - ver those that fear him;

SOPRANO
ALTO
as far as the east is from_ the west:_ so far has he

TENOR
BASS
set our sins from us. As a father is tender to - wards his child - ren:

so is the Lord ten - der to those___ that fear him.

SOPRANO

For he knows of what we are made:___ he remembers that we

are___ but dust. The days of man are but as grass:___ he flourishes

like___ a flower of the field;___ when the wind goes over it

TENOR & BASS

it___ is gone:___ and its place will know it no more.

SOPRANO
ALTO
But the merciful goodness of the Lord endures for ever and ever to-ward those that fear him:

TENOR & BASS

and his righteousness up - on___ their child - ren's child - ren;

All things I see

Haresfield 8 6 8 6 (CM)

Words: from Psalm 104
Brian Foley
Music: J Dykes Bower (1905–1981)

1 All things I see, Lord, call to me____ to
2 I see your beau - ty in the dawn,____ your
3 Your wa - ters ga - ther in the skies____ and
4 All things that grow, all things that live,____ and

speak their ma - ker's praise: how you have brought them
good - ness in the light; I see your power___ in
fall to fill the seas; your lands, the moun - tains
I my - self make known what praise, what glo - ry

all to be____ and guide them in____ their___ ways.
winds and storm,____ your wis - dom in____ the____ night.
where they rise,____ are or - dered as____ you____ please.
I must give____ to you, my God,___ a - lone.

Music: © Royal School of Church Music,
Addington Palace, Croydon, Surrey CR9 5AD

Words: from the *New Catholic Hymnal*
© 1971 Faber Music Ltd,
3 Queen Square, London WC1N 3AU

104A(ii)

All things I see

Southwell (Irons) 8 6 8 6 (CM)

Words: from Psalm 104
Brian Foley
Music: H S Irons (1834–1905)

1 All things I see, Lord, call to me to
2 I see your beau-ty in the dawn, your
3 Your wa-ters ga-ther in the skies and
4 All things that grow, all things that live, and

speak their ma-ker's praise: how you have brought them
good-ness in the light; I see your power in
fall to fill the seas; your lands, the moun-tains
I my-self make known what praise, what glo-ry

all to be and guide them in their ways.
winds and storm, your wis-dom in the night.
where they rise, are or-dered as you please.
I must give to you, my God, a - lone.

Words: from the *New Catholic Hymnal*
© 1971 Faber Music Ltd,
3 Queen Square, London WC1N 3AU

O bless the Lord, my soul

Brightwell Baldwin 8 6 8 6 (CM)

Words: from Psalm 104
Michael Perry
Music: John Barnard

1 'O bless the Lord, my soul!' I sing, and
2 For like a tent you spread the sky, on
MEN 3 You bind the sea, or loose the storm in

wor - ship day and night___ my God ar - rayed in
cha - riot-clouds you ride;___ and by the wind, your
light-ning's pri - mal flame;___ the ris - ing spring and

ma - jes - ty and robed in glo - rious light:
mes - sen - ger, your truth is pro - phe - sied.
flow - ing stream cry glo - ry to your name.

ALL
4 O mighty Lord of every land,
   you know our human need,
and all the creatures of the earth
   you guide and tend and feed.

WOMEN
5 The sun and moon appear and set
   controlled by hidden force;
the stars declare your faithfulness,
   consistent in their course.

ALL
6 Yet what you give, O sovereign Lord,
   your power can take away;
our life and death belong to you
   until our dying day.

7 So let me sing your worthy praise,
   your matchless grace extol
till all creation join the hymn:
   'O bless the Lord, my soul!'

Alternative tune: Bishopthorpe, *Psalms for Today* 92A(ii), *Hymns for Today's Church* 379

The majesty of mountains

Eythorne 7 6 8 6 8 6

Words: from Psalm 104
Michael Perry
Music: John Barnard

1 The ma-jes-ty of moun-tains, the__ sov-ereign-ty of skies,__ the__ re-gal rocks that arch a-bove where veils__ of va-pour rise,__ are gifts of God, the Lord of love, the__ wor-ship-ful, the wise.

2 The run-ning of the ri-ver, the__ surg-ing of the sea,__ the__ grass that grows high on the hill, the__ flower and fruit-ing tree,__ our Sav-iour sends us, by whose will all__ crea-tures came to be.

106A

Alleluia! Love eternal

South Ormsby 8 7 8 7 and Alleluias

Words: from Psalm 106
Paul Wigmore
Music: Paul Edwards

1 Al - le - lu - ia! Love e - ter - nal flows from
2 Though his peo - ple sinned a - gainst him, wor - shipped
3 Save us, Lord, in your great good - ness, hear us

God's most grac-ious heart. Who can show how great the Lord is? Where the
gods of wood and stone, he de - liv - ered, loved and blessed them! Was such
cal - ling, now as then; as our prais - es rise to greet you, let the

skill and where the art? Al - le - lu - ia, al - le - lu - ia!
mer - cy ev - er shown?
peo - ple say, 'A - men!'

Original key: G

Give God thanks

Cwm Rhondda 8 7 8 7 4 7 extended

Words: from Psalm 107
David Mowbray
Music: J Hughes (1873–1932)

1 'Give God thanks for he is gra-cious!' now may Is-rael
2 When God's peo-ple walked the des-ert, hun-gry, thir-sty,
3 Those who steer their ships through trou-ble, ride the storm and
4 Give God thanks for all his mer-cies: fields are wa-tered,

tru-ly say; through great tri-als he has brought us
faint of heart; he pre-pared for them a ci-ty,
plumb the deep, reach at length their pro-mised ha-ven,
crops are sown, sheep and cat-tle fill the pas-tures,

to the dawn of this new day.
gave them hope and took their part.
bless that grace which brings them sleep. All God's child-ren, all God's child-ren,
babes in arms have safe-ly grown.

praise the won-ders he has done (he has done), praise the won-ders he has done!

My heart is ready

108A

Horsell 8 6 8 6 (CM)

Words: from Psalm 108
Christopher Idle
Music: Gareth D Green

1 My heart is rea-dy, O my God: let songs of joy be born, let mu-sic sound from strings and voice – I will a-wake the dawn!

2 A-cross the con-ti-nents I sing, and grow-ing praise shall rise; for your great love spans earth and heaven, your truth sur-mounts the skies.

WOMEN 3 O God, be praised a-bove the heavens; let glo-ry fill the earth, and help and save with your right hand the race you brought to birth.

MEN

4 God speaks from his pure sanctuary
to claim both west and east:
'The plains and mountains all are mine,
the greatest and the least.'

WOMEN

5 'My people are my battle-dress,
my sceptre, helm, and sword;
while rebel nations have become
a footstool for the Lord!'

MEN

6 Who else can give us victory
and break the strongholds down?
O God, if you reject us now
we cannot fight alone.

ALL

7 How useless is all human help
when facing stubborn wrong!
But we shall triumph in the Lord,
and God shall be our song.

Alternative tune: St Fulbert, *Hymns for Today's Church* 168

Music: © Gareth D Green

Words: © Christopher Idle/Jubilate Hymns †

194

This is the word

Pokesdown 8 8 8 8 (LM)

Words: from Psalm 110
Brian Foley
Music: Michael Dawney

1 This is the word of God's de - cree, the
2 'That Ci - ty built for me of old, his
3 'A King to rule – my oath, my word! – a
4 'A Judge when earth - ly king - doms fall, to

voice of God who ev - er is: 'I send my Son, true
throne makes strong - er, ho - lier still; the Reign of Jus - tice,
great - er King than kings be - fore; a Priest to pray – and
speak his ver - dict on their ways; and then my Son, the

Son to me, to make all king - doms ev - er his!
long fore - told, this Son of mine will there ful - fil!
will be heard! – of high - est Priest - hood ev - er - more;
King of all, will bring to me his King - dom's praise!'

Alternative tune: Splendour, *Psalms for Today* 70, *Hymns for Today's Church* 118

111A   God's holy ways are just and true

Easter Song   8 8 4 4 8 8 and Alleluias

Words: from Psalm 111
Barbara Woollett
Music: *Geistliche Kirchengesang* Cologne 1623
adapted David Iliff

1 God's ho - ly ways are just and true, his
2 Bring back to mind his grace and love, our
3 Tell once a - gain his deeds of old, the

pro - mis - es are ev - er___ new, O___ praise___ him, al - le -
needs pro - vid - ed from a - bove; O___ praise___ him, al - le -
sto - ry of our migh - ty___ God, O___ praise___ him, al - le -

- lu - ia! Let ev - ery heart with prais - es
- lu - ia! He kept his word, and Je - sus
- lu - ia! For all his glo - rious works and

sing_____ and make this house with voi - ces
came_____ to make a peo - ple for his
ways_____ we shall re - joice through end - less

ring;____
name;____ O____ praise_ him, O____ praise_ him! Al - le -
days;____

-lu - ia,___ al - le - lu - ia, al - le - lu - ia!

112(i) How blessed are those who live by faith

Cross Deep 8 8 8 8 (LM)

Words: from Psalm 112
Michael Perry
Music: Barry Rose

UNISON

1 How blessed are those who live by faith, de-
2 How hap-py those who free-ly give, who
3 How joy-ful those who, strong for truth, re-
4 Then praise the Lord— let joy-ful praise to

-light-ing in God's sure com-mand; for rich in grace will
just-ly deal and kind-ly care; for in their dark-ness
-ly up-on the Lord most high; un-like the wick-ed
Fa-ther, Spi-rit, Son be given; to God who loved us,

be their homes, their child-ren migh-ty in the land:
light shall dawn, and long shall be their me-mory here:
they shall live, and lift their heads up to the sky!
came to save and fills our hearts with grace from heaven!

How blessed are those who live by faith 112(ii)

Morning Hymn 8 8 8 8 (LM)

Words: from Psalm 112
Michael Perry
Music: melody by F H Barthélémon (1741–1808)

1 How blessed are those who live by faith, de-
2 How hap-py those who free-ly give, who
3 How joy-ful those who, strong for truth, re-
4 Then praise the Lord – let joy-ful praise to

-light-ing in God's sure com-mand; for rich in grace will
just-ly deal and kind-ly care; for in their dark-ness
-ly up-on the Lord most high; un-like the wick-ed
Fa-ther, Spi-rit, Son be given; to God who loved us,

be their homes, their child-ren migh-ty in the land:
light shall dawn, and long shall be their me-mory here:
they shall live, and lift their heads up to the sky!
came to save and fills our hearts with grace from heaven!

113A   Servants of the living Lord

Slovenia 7 7 7 7 7 7

Words: from Psalm 113
Timothy Dudley-Smith
Music: Colin Evans

UNISON

1 Ser - vants of the living Lord, bend in awe be - fore his throne,_____ tell his ma - jes - ty a - broad,
2 Age to age, his name be blessed, An - cient of e - ter - nal days._____ Fur - thest bounds of east and west
3 Who like him in glo - ry reigns high - er than the heavens are high?_____ he who world on world sus - tains,
4 Lord of grace! In him we trust; by his love the lost are found,_____ low - ly lift - ed from the dust,

Alternative tune: St Petersburg, *Psalms for Today* 25A

Music: © Colin Evans

know and name him God a - lone.
e - cho his per - pet - ual praise:
sun and stars and sea and sky:
hap - py homes with child - ren crowned.

Join to praise the
ev - er - liv - ing
he it is who,
All who stand be -

Lord of grace, all who stand be - fore his
Lord of grace, throned be - yond all time and
Lord of grace, hears from heaven, his dwell - ing -
- fore his face, praise, O praise, the Lord of

vv 1-3

face.
space.
- place.

v 4

grace!

114   When Israel broke their cruel chains

Dundee 8 6 8 6 (CM)

Words: from Psalm 114
David Mowbray
Music: *Scottish Psalter* Edinburgh 1615

1 When Is - rael broke their cru - el chains and
2 When Is - rael crossed the ri - ver's edge and
3 Now we, through Christ who goes be - fore, stand

E - gypt lost the day, the Lord's own peo - ple
reached the pro - mised land, they felt in their de -
firm on so - lid ground; we sing God's praise, and

sang for joy and laughed up - on their way.
-liv - er - ance the touch of___ God's good hand.
all the earth shall trem - ble___ at the sound.

Not to us be glory given

Lux Eoi 8 7 8 7 D

Words: from Psalm 115
Timothy Dudley-Smith
Music: A Sullivan (1842–1900)

1 Not to us be glo-ry giv-en but to him who reigns a-bove.
2 Not what hu-man fin-gers fash-ion, gold and sil-ver, deaf and blind,
3 Not in them is hope of bless-ing— hope is in the liv-ing Lord!
4 Not the dead, but we the liv-ing praise the Lord with all our powers;

Glo-ry to the God of hea-ven for his faith-ful-ness and love!
dead to know-ledge and com-pas-sion, hav-ing nei-ther heart nor mind—
High and low, his name con-fess-ing, find in him their shield and sword;
of his good-ness free-ly giv-ing— his is hea-ven; earth is ours.

What though un-be-liev-ing voi-ces hear no word and see no sign,
life-less gods, some yet a-dore them, nerve-less hands and feet of clay;
hope of all whose hearts re-vere him, God of Is-rael, still the same!
Not to us be glo-ry giv-en but to him who reigns a-bove.

still in God my heart re-joic-es, work-ing out his will di-vine.
all be-come, who bow be-fore them, lost in-deed, and dead as they.
God of Aa-ron! Those who fear him, he re-mem-bers them by name.
Glo-ry to the God of hea-ven, for his faith-ful-ness and love!

Alternative tune: Alleluia, *Psalms for Today* 34A, *Hymns for Today's Church* 428

203

Words: © Timothy Dudley-Smith

116A(i) I love the Lord, he heard my voice

Carter Knowle 8 8 8 8 8 8

Words: from Psalm 116
Barbara Woollett
Music: Derek Williams

Refrain

Let love to love re-spond and_ say, 'O praise the Lord with me to-day!'

Verses

1 I love the Lord, he heard my voice,   he list-ened when I called his name;
2 When dark des-pair en-tan-gled me,   in depths of grief I called his name;
3 I cried with sor-row ma-ny tears —   in guil-ty dread I called his name;

in thank-ful-ness I shall re-joice   his grace and mer-cy to pro-claim.
from sin and death he set me free,   and to my res-cue Je-sus came.
but God for-gave my doubts and fears,   he told me Je-sus took the blame:

4 Now that I know he answers prayer,
with child-like trust I'll call his name;
when there is no one else to care
his steadfast love will stay the same.
Let love to love . . .

5 Turn to the Lord, his word obey,
lift up your voice and call his name;
ask him to lead you in his way —
his promised love is yours to claim:
Let love to love . . .

The refrain can be sung in 4-part harmony.

I love the Lord, he heard my voice 116A(ii)

St Matthias 888888

Words: from Psalm 116
Barbara Woollett
Music: W H Monk (1823–1889)

1 I love the Lord, he heard my voice, he list-ened when I
2 When dark des-pair en-tan-gled me, in depths of grief I
3 I cried with sor-row ma-ny tears – in guil-ty dread I

called his name; in thank-ful-ness I shall re-joice his
called his name; from sin and death he set me free, and
called his name; but God for-gave my doubts and fears, he

grace and mer-cy to pro-claim.
to my res-cue Je-sus came. Let love to love re-
told me Je-sus took the blame:

-spond and say, 'O praise the Lord with me to-day!'

4 Now that I know he answers prayer,
with child-like trust I'll call his name;
when there is no one else to care
his steadfast love will stay the same.
   Let love to love . . .

5 Turn to the Lord, his word obey,
lift up your voice and call his name;
ask him to lead you in his way –
his promised love is yours to claim:
   Let love to love . . .

Words: Barbara Woollett/Jubilee Hymns †

205

How can I repay the Lord

Words: Psalm 116
adapted from *The Liturgical Psalter*
David Frost and others
Music: Stephen Dean and John Barnard

How can I repay the Lord
for all the goodness he shows to me?

1 I love the Lord because he ' heard my ' voice:
   the ' voice of · my ' suppli'cation;
2 because he in'clined his ' ear to me:
   in the ' day ' that I ' called to him.
     How can I repay . . .

3 The cords of death encompassed me
   the snares of the ' grave took ' hold on me:
   I ' was in ' anguish · and ' sorrow.
4 Then I called upon the ' name · of the ' Lord:
   'O ' Lord · I be'seech you · de'liver me!'
     How can I repay . . .

5 Gracious and righteous ' is the ' Lord:
   full of com'passion ' is our ' God.
6 The Lord pre'serves the ' simple:
   when ' I was · brought ' low he ' saved me.
     How can I repay . . .

7 Return O my ' soul · to your ' rest:
   for the ' Lord ' has re'warded you.
8 For you O Lord have delivered my ' soul from ' death:
   my eyes from ' tears · and my ' feet from ' falling.
     How can I repay . . .

There should be no pause between the end of the verses
and the start of the introduction to the Refrain.

Praise the Lord, all nations, praise

Veni Sancte Spiritus 7 7 7 D

Words: from Psalm 117
Christopher Idle
Music: later form of melody by
S Webbe the elder (1740–1816)

Praise the Lord, all na - tions, praise; wor - ship God, all hu - man-kind:

Al - le - lu - ia, praise the Lord! Migh - ty is your love_ for us,

firm for ev - er is your truth: Al - le - lu - ia, praise the Lord!

Praise him, you nations

Laudate Dominum

Words: from Psalm 117
Taizé
Words and music: Jacques Berthier

A Verses

SOLO/CHOIR

1 Praise the Lord, all you na-tions; praise him, all you peo-ples. Al - le - lu - ia!

B Strong is his love and mer-cy; he is faith-ful for ev - er. Al - le - lu - ia!

A 2 Al-le-lu - ia, al-le-lu - ia: let ev - ery-thing liv-ing give praise to the Lord.

B Al - le - lu - ia, al-le - lu - ia: let ev - ery-thing liv-ing give praise to the Lord.

Coda

The Refrain is intended to act as an accompaniment to the Verses:
A and B indicate coinciding points in Verse and Refrain.

118A(i) Open the gates of righteousness

Sennen Cove 8 6 8 6 (CM)

Words: from Psalm 118
David Mowbray
Music: W H Harris (1883–1973)

1 O - pen the gates of right - eous - ness, for
2 When we were trapped at ev - ery turn, hard -
3 The rock the build - ers had re - fused be -
4 En - ter God's house to praise his name, and

we have come to pray; to of - fer thanks for
- pressed on ev - ery side, the Lord our God came
- came the cor - ner - stone: who can de - ny this
all his tri - umphs tell; sal - ute the peo - ple

all God's gifts with - in his house to - day.
to our help and all our bonds un - tied.
is a thing the Lord him - self has done?
of the Lord = Be - loved, we wish you well!

Open the gates of righteousness 118A(ii)

Chorus Angelorum 8 6 8 6 (CM)

Words: from Psalm 118
David Mowbray
Music: A Somervell (1863–1937)

1 O - pen the gates__ of right - eous - ness,_____ for we have
2 When we were trapped at ev - ery turn,_____ hard-pressed on
3 The rock the build - ers had__ re - fused_____ be - came the
4 En - ter God's house__ to praise__ his name,_____ and all his

come_____ to pray;_____ to of - fer thanks__ for
ev - ery side,_____ the Lord__ our God__ came
cor - ner - stone:_____ who can__ de - ny____ this
tri - umphs tell;_____ sal - ute__ the peo - ple

all_____ God's gifts__ with - in__ his house_____ to - day.
to_____ our help__ and all__ our bonds_____ un - tied.
is_____ a thing__ the Lord__ him - self_____ has done?
of_____ the Lord – Be - loved,__ we wish_____ you well!

119A

The will of God

University 8 6 8 6 (CM)

Words: from Psalm 119
Timothy Dudley-Smith
Music: C Collignon (1725–1785)

1 The will of God to mark my way, the
2 Your eyes of mer - cy keep me still, your
3 With or - dered step se - cure and strong, from
4 So set my heart to love your word and

word of God for light; e - ter - nal jus - tice
gra - cious love be mine; so work in me your
sin's op - pres - sion freed, re - deemed from ev - ery
ev - ery pro - mise prove, to walk with truth be -

to o - bey in ev - er - last - ing right.
per - fect will and cause your face to shine.
kind of wrong in thought and word and deed –
- fore the Lord in right - eous - ness and love.

With all my heart I seek

Ibstone 6 6 6 6

Words: from Psalm 119
David Mowbray
Music: M Tiddeman (1837–1915)

1 With all my heart I seek the true and liv-ing___ way!
2 Let me not wa-ver now from sim-ple hon-es - ty,
3 Your laws and your com-mands re - main my great de - light;
4 Through youth and through old age, Lord, may I not for - get

Lord, guide these steps of mine or I shall go a - stray.
or fail in my re - solve to keep in - te - gri - ty.
I speak of them at noon and pon - der them at___ night.
that in your match-less word, there love and truth have_ met.

119C Blessed are those whose way is blameless

Words: from Psalm 119
from *The Liturgical Psalter*
David Frost and others
Music: E J Hopkins (1818–1901)

Blessed are those whose ' way is ' blameless:
who ' walk · in the ' law · of the ' Lord.
Blessed are those who ' keep · his com'mands:
and seek him ' with their ' whole ' heart.

I have treasured your ' words · in my ' heart:
that I ' might not ' sin a'gainst you.
Blessed are ' you Lord ' God:
O ' teach me ' your ' statutes.

With my lips I ' have been ' telling:
all the ' judgements ' of your ' mouth;
and I find more joy in the way of ' your com'mands:
than in ' all ' manner · of ' riches.

Guide me in the path of ' your com'mandments:
for there'in is ' my de'light.
The law of your mouth is ' dearer · to ' me:
than a ' wealth of ' gold and ' silver.

Lord how I ' love your ' law:
it is my medi'tation ' all the · day ' long.
How sweet are your ' words · to my ' tongue:
sweeter than ' honey ' to my ' mouth.

Your word is a lantern ' to my ' feet:
and a ' light ' to my ' path.
Your commands are my in'heritance · for ' ever:
they ' are the ' joy of · my ' heart.

Glory to the Father and ' to the ' Son:
and ' to the ' Holy ' Spirit;
as it was in the be'ginning · is ' now:
and shall be for ' ever. 'A'men.

I see the mountains far away

Eureka 8 8 8 8 (LM)

Words: from Psalm 121
Brian Foley
Music: from *The Good Old Songs* 1913
arranged David Iliff

1 I see the moun - tains far a - way, the____
2 I look be - yond fa - mil - iar things, be -
3 Yet God is pre - sent where I am, a____
4 My place in his - tory and my name, my____

bor - ders of the____ world I know, where____ God, it seems, must____
-yond the li - mits____ set for me,____ to____ where, it seems, God____
hid - den God, though__ ev - er near,__ not____ one who lives and____
years, my days, and____ all they bring – in____ these I see God's__

live a - lone in____ pla - ces where I may not go!
hides him - self, too____ far, too deep, in se - cre - cy!
loves a - lone, but____ God, my God, who loves me here.
will for me, his____ love for me, in ev - ery - thing.

Alternative tune: Angels' Song, *Hymns for Today's Church* 306

121B   I lift my eyes

Davos 9 8 9 7

Words: from Psalm 121
Timothy Dudley-Smith
Music: Michael Baughen and Elisabeth Crocker
arranged John Barnard

1 I lift my eyes_____ to the qui - et hills_____ in the
2 I lift my eyes_____ to the qui - et hills_____ to a
4 I lift my eyes_____ to the qui - et hills_____ and my

press of a bu - sy day;   as green hills stand_____
calm that is mine to share;   se - cure and still_____
heart to the Fa - ther's throne;   in all my ways_____

in a dus - ty land   so   God_____ is my strength and stay.
in the Fa - ther's will   and   kept_____ by the Fa - ther's care.
to the end of days   the   Lord_____ will pre - serve his own.

216

The Harmony version is harmonically compatible with the Unison setting.

I will lift up my eyes to the hills

From Psalm 121
Words and music: Mark Pallant
and Steven Brazier

The accompaniment for verse 1 is also suitable for verses 2 and 3.

The accompaniment may be sung in harmony (alto, tenor and bass) to *Ah*.

slum - ber;___ he who watch - es o - ver

Is - ra - el will nei - ther slum - ber___ nor sleep.

2 The Lord, he is your___ guard - ian,___ the

Lord is your de-fence at your right hand;___ the sun will not harm. you. by

day___ nor the moon___ by night.

3 The Lord will pro - tect you from all dan - ger,___

he will watch o - ver_ your life;___ the Lord will guard your com-ing and your

go - ing,_ both now___ and for ev - er - more._

Refrain after verse 3 overleaf

219

121c **I will lift up my eyes to the hills**

I lift up my eyes to the hills

Words: Psalm 121
from *The Liturgical Psalter*
David Frost and others
Music: Barry Rose

1 I lift up my ' eyes · to the ' hills:
but ' where · shall I ' find ' help?
2 My help ' comes · from the ' Lord:
who has ' made ' heaven · and ' earth.

3 He will not suffer your ' foot to ' stumble:
and he who watches ' over · you ' will not ' sleep.
4 Be sure he who has ' charge of ' Israel:
will ' neither ' slumber · nor ' sleep.

5 The Lord him'self is · your ' keeper:
the Lord is your defence up'on your ' right ' hand;
6 the sun shall not ' strike you · by ' day:
nor ' shall the ' moon by ' night.

7 The Lord will defend you from ' all ' evil:
it is ' he · who will ' guard your ' life.
8 The Lord will defend your going out and your ' coming ' in:
from this time ' forward · for ' ever'more.

**Glory to the Father and ' to the ' Son:
and ' to the ' Holy' Spirit;
as it was in the be'ginning · is ' now:
and shall be for ' ever. ' A'men.**

Set for Her Majesty the Queen's Jubilee Service in St Paul's Cathedral, 7th June 1977.
Original key: F

122A   I rejoiced to hear them say

St George's, Windsor   7 7 7 7 D

Words: from Psalm 122
Basil Bridge
Music: G J Elvey (1816–1893)

1 I re-joiced to hear them say, 'Come and wor-ship God to-day!
2 Here in gra-ti-tude we bring all we are to serve our King;
3 God, the Lord of peace, is near – come in faith, and meet him here;

Come, with heart and mind and soul, seek the peace that makes us whole;
his for-give-ness we en-treat in whom love and jus-tice meet:
let each rest-less soul be still, glad to know and do his will:

see dis-or-dered lives re-stored in the pre-sence of the Lord:
bring our needs to him in prayer, ask his help, and trust his care;
as a ci-ty's walls and towers of-fered safe-ty – God is ours!

from your bur-dens find re-lease; in his pre-sence there is peace.'
join with all, in ev-ery place, who have sought and known his grace.
There-fore we re-joice, and say, 'Come and wor-ship God to-day!'

Jerusalem! How glad I was

Durrow 8 6 8 6 D (DCM)

Words: from Psalm 122
Christopher Idle
Music: Irish traditional melody
arranged John Barnard

1 Je - ru - sa - lem! How glad I was when they in - vit - ed me
2 Je - ru - sa - lem! A ci - ty built com - pact and walled a - round;
3 Je - ru - sa - lem! May you have peace, your peo - ple long en - dure;

to climb with them the mount of prayer, the place of ma - jes - ty:
the sa - cred tribes as - cend - ed here and made their psalms re - sound.
may all your ci - ti - zens be safe, your towers and streets se - cure.

Je - ru - sa - lem! With - in your gates our will - ing feet have stood,
Let us, like Is - ra - el, go up to pay the Lord our dues,
For bro - thers, sis - ters, friends, I pray let peace re - turn a - gain:

and there we raised our voic - es high to fill the house of God.
to hear the judge - ments of the law, the joy of God's good news.
O Lord our God, meet us in grace, in glo - ry come to reign!

Alternative tune: Kingsfold, *Hymns for Today's Church* 457

123A(i)   I lift my eyes to you

West Wickham 6 6 8 6 (SM)

Words: from Psalm 123
Christopher Idle
Music: Alan Ridout

1 I lift____ my eyes____ to you, to heaven your
2 Have mer - cy, Lord,____ we pray, and hear your
3 The proud__ have mocked____ us long, their scorn we

roy - al throne: as ser - vants watch____ their
peo - ple's cries: un - til____ your mer - cy
have____ en - dured; our days____ are filled____ with

mas - ter's hand we look____ to you a - lone.
reach - es us on you____ we fix our eyes.
their con - tempt: we look____ to you, O Lord.

I lift my eyes to you

123A(ii)

St Michael 6 6 8 6 (SM)

Words: from Psalm 123
Christopher Idle
Music: *Genevan Psalter* 1551
adapted W Crotch (1775–1847)

1 I lift my eyes to you, to
2 Have mer - cy, Lord, we pray, and
3 The proud have mocked us long, their

heaven your roy - al throne: as ser - vants watch their
hear your peo - ple's cries: un - til your mer - cy
scorn we have en - dured; our days are filled with

mas - ter's hand we look___ to you a - lone.
reach - es us on you___ we fix our eyes.
their con - tempt: we look___ to you, O Lord.

123B   Master, we lift our eyes

Little Venice   4 5 4 5 D

Words: from Psalm 123
David Mowbray
Music: G H Knight (1908–1979)

1 Mas - ter, we lift____ our eyes, ex - pect - ing__ your pro-mised gift,____
2 Tri - ni - ty strong,____ source of all bless - ing: joy - ful our song,____

your arm pro - tect - ing: though some have lied,____ our__ faith des - pis - ing =
wor - ship ex - press - ing; Fa - ther and Son,__ Spi - rit life - giv - er:__

you are our guide,____ rest - ing and ris - ing.
your will be done,____ now and for ev - er.

If the Lord had not been near

Anderson 7 7 7 5

Words: from Psalm 124
Paul Wigmore
Music: Jane Marshall

UNISON

1 If_____ the Lord had not been near,
2 If_____ the Lord had not come in,
3 If_____ the Lord who set us free
4 Swift_____ and cer - tain to our aid

at_____ our side and quick to hear, who__ would then have
strong to save from dead - ly sin, who__ would then have
did__ not hear us, could not see, who__ would then our
comes the one by whom were made star - ry hea - vens,

calmed our fear?
helped__ us win?
sav - iour be? Let us praise the Lord!_____
wood - land glade.

Original key: D♭

124A(ii)   If the Lord had not been near

Capetown 7 7 7 5

Words: from Psalm 124
Paul Wigmore
Music: F Filitz (1804–1876)

1 If the Lord had not been near, at our side and
2 If the Lord had not come in, strong to save from
3 If the Lord who set us free did not hear us,
4 Swift and cer - tain to our aid comes the one by

quick___ to hear,_____ who would then have
dead - ly sin,_____ who would then have
could___ not see,_____ who would then our
whom___ were made_____ star - ry hea - vens,

calmed our fear?____
helped us win?____   Let us praise the Lord!
sav - iour be?____
wood - land glade.____

Those who rely on the Lord

125

Was lebet 12 10 12 10

Words: from Psalm 125
Christopher Idle
Music: melody from manuscript
by J H Rheinhardt, Üttingen (1754)

1 Those who__ re - ly on the Lord are un - shake - ab - le,
2 E - vil__ shall not al - ways rule o - ver right - eous-ness,

firm__ as mount Zi - on, su - preme - ly as - sured;
God's__ time will come when op - press - ion shall cease:

just as__ the moun - tains en - cir - cle Je - ru - sa - lem,
Lord, bless__ the right - eous, re - strain the im - pe - ni - tent,

round us for ev - er is stand - ing the Lord.
grant to your peo - ple the gift of your peace.

126A
Laughter and song

Vossem 10 10

Words: from Psalm 126
David Mowbray
Music: David Iliff

1 Laugh - ter and song! The Lord has done great things: his
peo - ple once were freed from ty - rant kings.

2 Yet now we wait in___ sad cap - ti - vi - ty: rise
up, re - deem - ing Lord, to set___ us free!

3 Tears turn to joy! The___ weep - ing farm - er sows and,
slow - ly through the storms, the har - vest grows.

The Unison and Harmony versions are not harmonically compatible.

Alternative tune: Song 46, *Psalms for Today* 68A, *Hymns for Today's Church* 149

When the Lord turned again

Words: Psalm 126
from *The Liturgical Psalter*
David Frost and others

126B

J Turle (1802–1882)

T A Walmisley (1814–1856)

1 When the Lord turned again the ˈ fortunes · of ˈ Zion:
 then were we like ˈ men reˈstored to ˈ life.

2 Then was our mouth ˈ filled with ˈ laughter:
 and ˈ our ˈ tongue with ˈ singing.

3 Then said they aˈmong the ˈ heathen:
 'The Lord has ˈ done great ˈ things for ˈ them.'

4 Truly the Lord has done great ˈ things for ˈ us:
 and ˈ therefore ˈ we reˈjoiced.

5 Turn again our ˈ fortunes · O ˈ Lord:
 as the streams reˈturn · to the ˈ dry ˈ south.

6 Those that ˈ sow in ˈ tears:
 shall ˈ reap with ˈ songs of ˈ joy.

Second part

7 He who goes out weeping ˈ bearing · the ˈ seed:
 **shall come again in gladness ˈ
 bringing · his ˈ sheaves ˈ with him.**

 **Glory to the Father and ˈ to the ˈ Son:
 and ˈ to the ˈ Holy ˈ Spirit;
 as it was in the beˈginning · is ˈ now:
 and shall be for ˈ ever. ˈ Aˈmen.**

If God is building when we build

Land of Rest 8 6 8 6 (CM)

Words: from Psalms 127 and 124
Brian Foley
Music: American folk melody
arranged John Barnard

1 If God__ is build - ing when__ we build,__ the
2 If God__ is guard - ing when__ we guard,__ he
3 If God__ is work - ing when__ we work__ to

house__ we raise__ will stand;_____ if God__ de - signs__ when
keeps__ the watch we keep,_____ pro - tects__ our ways,__ pro-
make__ the things we make;_____ he gives__ ap - pro - val

we__ de - sign,__ his skill__ is in____ our hand:____
-vides__ our days__ the har - vest that__ we reap:____
and__ suc - cess__ to la - bour for__ his sake:____

4 If God is speaking when we speak,
  our words become his word,
  and in the speech of everyday,
  eternal things are heard:

5 If God is building when we build,
  we call each work our own,
  but not for us to praise ourselves –
  our praise is God alone!

If God is building when we build　127A(ii)

McKee　8 6 8 6 (CM)

Words: from Psalms 127 and 124
Brian Foley
Music: American melody
arranged H T Burleigh (1866–1949)

1 If____ God is build - ing____ when we build, the
2 If____ God is guard - ing____ when we guard, he
3 If____ God is work - ing____ when we work to

house we raise_ will_ stand;_____ if____ God de - signs_ when
keeps the watch we_ keep,_____ pro - tects our_ ways, pro -
make the things we_ make;_____ he_ gives ap - pro - val

we____ de - sign, his____ skill____ is in____ our hand:
- vides_ our_ days the___ har - vest that___ we reap:
and____ suc - cess to____ la - bour for___ his sake:

4 If God is speaking when we speak,
　our words become his word,
　and in the speech of everyday,
　eternal things are heard:

5 If God is building when we build,
　we call each work our own,
　but not for us to praise ourselves –
　our praise is God alone!

127B   Unless the Lord has built the house

Hemsby   8 6 8 6 (CM)

Words: from Psalm 127
David Mowbray
Music: Mervyn Horder

UNISON OR HIGH VOICES

1 Un - less the Lord __ has built the house __ it must be __ built a - gain; __
2 What va - lue has __ a life of haste, __ of end - less, an - xious toil? __
3 A - mong God's gifts, __ a hap - py home __ a bless-ing __ rich __ in - deed; __
4 That home, that house, __ as years go by __ must wea-ther storm and strain:

LOW VOICES (OPTIONAL)

ex - cept the Lord __ de-fends a __ town its watch-men wake in __ vain. __
God has for those __ who keep his __ law a gar - land none can __ spoil: __
a joy-ful, lov - ing part-ner - ship, a strength to those in __ need. __
un - less the Lord __ has built the __ house it must be built a - gain. __

Alternative tune: Albano, *Hymns for Today's Church* 135

Music: © Mervyn Horder

234

Blessed are those who fear the Lord 128A

Innocents 7 7 7 7

Words: from Psalm 128
Christopher Idle
Music: *The Parish Choir* 1850

1 Blessed are those who fear the Lord, walk-ing
2 Bless-ings greet the hus-band, wife, par-ents,
3 Bless us, Lord! Your king-dom come; child-ren's

in God's per-fect ways; all they do shall bring re-
child-ren, old and young; fruits of faith be theirs for
child-ren learn your praise: prayer in na-tion, church and

-ward, love en-rich-es all their days.
life, joy in songs to-ge-ther sung.
home, peace in Christ to crown our days.

128B   Bless all who trust in God

Doncaster 6 6 8 6 (SM)

Words: from Psalm 128
David Mowbray
Music: S Wesley (1766–1837)

1 Bless all who trust in God and
2 Let mar - riag - es be strong and
3 And since we may not boast such

walk with - in God's ways; bless ev - ery soul whose
spar - kle bright as wine; let part - ners and let
joys are ours by right, teach us, good Lord, to

hap - pi - ness springs from the Lord's own praise!
child - ren thrive and flour - ish like the vine!
take your gifts with thanks and with de - light.

Alternative tune: Sandys, *Hymns for Today's Church* 493

Out of our failure to create

Billing 8 6 8 6 (CM)

Words: from Psalm 130
Fred Kaan
Music: R R Terry (1865–1938)

1 Out of our fail - ure to_____ cre - ate a
2 Out of the dark - ness of_____ our time, of
3 Out of the depths we cry_____ to him whose
4 Hope in the Lord whose time - less love gives

world_ of love_ and care; out of_____ the_ depths of
days_ for ev - er gone, our souls_ are_ long - ing
will_ is strong_ and just; all hu - man hole - and -
laugh - ter where_ we wept; the 'Fa - ther, who_ at

hu - man life_____ we cry_____ to God_ in prayer.
for_____ the light,_ like watch - men for_____ the dawn.
- cor - ner ways_ are by_____ his light_ ex - posed.
ev - ery point_ his word_ has given_ and kept.

Alternative tune: Gerontius, *Hymns for Today's Church* 140

130B   Up from the depths I cry to God

Macpherson's Farewell   8 6 8 6 D (DCM)

Words: from Psalm 130
Christopher Idle
Music: Scottish traditional melody
arranged David Iliff

1 Up from the depths I___ cry_ to_ God: O___ lis-ten, Lord, to me;
2 If you, my God, should mea-sure guilt who then could ev-er stand?
3 O Is-rael, set your hope on_ God whose mer-cy is su - preme:

O_ hear my_ voice in___ this_ dis-tress, this_ mire of mi - se - ry.
But_ those who fear your name will find for - give-ness from your hand.
the_ na - tion mourn-ing___ for_ its_ sin he sure-ly will_ re - deem.

I___ wait for God with all my heart, my_ hope is in___ his___ word;_

and_ more than watch-men for the dawn I'm_ long-ing for_ the_ Lord.

Alternative tune: Kingsfold, *Hymns for Today's Church* 457

Out of the depths I cry

130c

Growing 6 6 6 6

Words: from Psalm 130
David Mowbray
Music: Robin Sheldon

1 Out of the depths I___ cry:___ O God, re - mem - ber
2 If you watch si - lent - ly___ and mark things done a -
3 At such a time as___ this___ my soul waits for the
4 With - out his sav - ing___ word,___ all hope for ev - er

me! What earth - ly help__ have__ I___ if you watch
- miss, to__ whom then may__ I__ fly___ at such a___
Lord; no__ joy is there, no__ bliss___ with - out his__
dies: speak now, most migh - ty__ Lord,___ and from the__

vv 1-3

si - lent - ly?___
time as__ this?___
sav - ing__ word.

v 4

depths I__ rise!___

Alternative tune: Eccles, *Hymns for Today's Church* 409

131A   Before the Lord my soul is bowed

Herongate   8 8 8 8 (LM)

Words: from Psalm 131
Stephen Horsfall
Music: English traditional melody
collected R Vaughan Williams (1872–1958)
arranged David Iliff

1 Be - fore the Lord my soul is bowed in
2 But I have made my spi - rit calm; my
3 Let grate - ful voi - ces tell a - broad the

trust and quiet hu - mi - li - ty; I do not let my
soul is like a child at rest who knows that it is
migh - ty name that we a - dore: O Is - rael, hope in

heart grow proud or pon - der things too great for me.
safe from harm and sleeps up - on its mo - ther's breast.
God the Lord, your glo - ry now and ev - er - more!

Lord, this thing I ask you

Belgravia 6 5 6 5

Words: from Psalm 131
David Mowbray
Music: Gareth D Green

1 Lord, this thing I ask you:
2 All God's sons and daugh - ters

hold in check my pride, as a child o - be - dient
to his heart are dear: let them now and al - ways

at its mo - ther's side.
trust, and ne - ver fear.

Alternative tune: North Coates, *Psalms for Today* 162B(ii), *Hymns for Today's Church* 384

132 As David took no rest

Elmore 8 6 8 6 (CM)

Words: from Psalm 132
David Mowbray
Music: Anthony Greening

1 As Da - vid took no rest un - til he housed the ark se - cure,
2 As Da - vid trust - ed God to set an heir up - on his throne,
3 A - rise, O Lord, and come to - day in your great power and might;

so in the work - ing of God's will may we by faith en - dure.
so may God's peo - ple ne - ver doubt that jus - tice will be done.
crown all your cho - sen ones with joy and lead us in - to light!

Alternative tune: Irish, *Hymns for Today's Church* 363

How good a thing it is

Steeple Ashton 6 6 8 6 (SM)

Words: from Psalm 133
J E Seddon (1915–1983)
Music: John Barnard

1 How good a thing it is, how
2 As per - fume, by its scent, breathes
3 And like re - fresh - ing dew that
4 God grants the choic - est gifts to

plea - sant to be - hold, when all God's peo - ple
fra - grance all a - round, so life it - self will
falls up - on the hills, true un - ion sheds its
those who live in peace; to them such bless - ings

live at one, the law of love up - hold!
sweet - er be where u - ni - ty is found.
gen - tle grace, and deep - er love in - stils.
shall a - bound and ev - er - more in - crease.

133A(ii)

How good a thing it is

Venice 6 6 8 6 (SM)

Words: from Psalm 133
J E Seddon (1915–1983)
Music: W Amps (1824–1910)

1 How good a thing it is, how
2 As per-fume, by its scent, breathes
3 And like re-fresh-ing dew that
4 God grants the choic-est gifts to

plea-sant to be-hold, when all God's peo-ple
fra-grance all a-round, so life it-self will
falls up-on the hills, true u-nion sheds its
those who live in peace; to them such bless-ings

live at one, the law of love up-hold!
sweet-er be where u-ni-ty is found.
gen-tle grace, and deep-er love in-stils.
shall a-bound and ev-er-more in-crease.

Behold how pleasant

Cornwall 8 8 6 8 8 6

Words: from Psalm 133
Keith Landis
Music: S S Wesley (1810–1876)

1 Be - hold how__ plea - sant it shall__ be for__
2 Like pre - cious__ oil poured on each__ head, like__

those who dwell in u - ni - ty as__ chil - dren of the__
dew up - on mount Zi - on shed, his__ mer - cies free - ly__

Lord; though not by na - ture so in - clined, they
flow; and ev - en more, the Lord com - mands the

have in Christ one heart and__ mind, mi - ra - cu - lous ac - cord!
fair - est bles - sing of his__ hands – e - ter - nal life to__ know!

134A Bless the Lord as day departs

Asthall 7 8 7 8

Words: from Psalm 134,
Come bless the Lord
Timothy Dudley-Smith
Music: John Barnard

DESCANT

3 So may we who watch or rest bless the Lord of

1 Bless the Lord as day de-parts; let your lamps be
2 As with-in the dark-ened shrine, faith-ful to their
3 So may we who watch or rest bless the Lord of

earth and hea-ven; and by him our-selves be blessed,

bright-ly burn-ing, lift-ing ho-ly hands and hearts
sa-cred call-ing, sons and priests of Le-vi's line
earth and hea-ven; and by him our-selves be blessed,

grace and peace and mer-cy giv - en.

to the Lord, till day's re-turn - ing.
blessed the Lord as night was fall - ing:
grace and peace and mer-cy giv - en.

Come, praise the Lord

Les Commandemens 9 8 9 8

Words: from Psalm 134,
Come bless the Lord
Christopher Idle
Music: L Bourgeois (c1510–c1561)
arranged mainly by C Goudimel (c1514–1572)

1 Come, praise the Lord, all you his ser - vants, who stand with - in his
2 Come, bless the Lord, all those who love him, who serve with - in the

house by night; come lift your hands and hearts in
ho - ly place; may God who made both earth and

wor - ship, God be your praise and your de - light.
hea - ven grant us the bless - ings of his grace.

Alternative tune: Spiritus Vitae, *Hymns for Today's Church* 43

Come bless the Lord

Words: from Psalm 134
Come bless the Lord
from *The Liturgical Psalter*
David Frost and others

J Stainer (1840–1901)

J Jones (1728–1796)

1 Come bless the Lord all you ╎ servants · of the ╎ Lord:
 you that by night ╎ stand · in the ╎ house of · our ╎ God.

2 Lift up your hands toward the holy place and ╎ bless the ╎ Lord:
 may the Lord bless you from Zion
 the ╎ Lord who · made ╎ heaven · and ╎ earth.

 Glory to the Father and ╎ to the ╎ Son:
 and ╎ to the ╎ Holy ╎ Spirit;
 as it was in the be╎ginning · is ╎ now:
 and shall be for ╎ ever. ╎ A╎men.

Give thanks to God

Lyminge 8 8 7 D

Words: from Psalm 136
Paul Wigmore
Music: John Barnard

1 Give thanks to God, the Lord of all cre - a - tion's won - ders,
2 And to the joy of hu - man eye be - yond the earth he
3 And from op - press - ion's e - vil spell he led his peo - ple
4 Give thanks to God, the God of all, for he is good, he

great and small, whose
set the sky – his   love en - dures for ev - er:_____
Is - ra - el – his
hears our call, his

he gave the splen - dour of the earth, the birth of spring, the
he blessed the dark - ness with the light, the sun by day, the
through sea and de - sert, pain and fear their strength was his, for
our God is from e - ter - ni - ty, he lifts and feeds us,

Organ

win - ter's death –
stars by night –   his__ love en - dures for ev - er.
he was near –
sets us free –

137A

By rivers of sorrow

Streets of Laredo   12 11 12 11

Words: from Psalms 137 and 138
Michael Perry
Music: American traditional melody
arranged Noël Tredinnick
Descant: David Iliff

UNISON

1 By ri - vers of sor - row we sat and re - mem-bered the ci - ty of
2 O how shall we sing in the an - guish of ex - ile – the songs of the
3 You daugh-ter of Ba - by - lon, doomed to des - truc - tion, you peo - ple of

hap - pi - ness where we be - long; our harps and our me - lo - dies
Lord in a far a - way land? Je - ru - sa - lem, see if I
E - dom who throw down our walls, be warned of the judge-ment on

hung in the branch - es, and there our tor - men-tors de - mand-ed a song!
ev - er for - get you till death take my voice and the skill of my hand!
you and your child - ren: when blas-phem - y fails and when ty - ran - ny falls.

138A

I'll praise you, Lord

Highwood 11 10 11 10

Words: from Psalm 138
Michael Perry
Music: R R Terry (1865–1938)

1 I'll praise you, Lord, with heart content and joyful,
be - fore the world I'll tell your right-eous ways;
I will bow down to-wards your holy tem - ple,
and breathe your name and sing your wor - thy praise.

2 Be - yond the skies you set your time-less king - dom =
your word shall last, your throne shall ne - ver fall;
the lords of earth will mar - vel at your wis - dom
and kneel be - fore the migh - ty Lord of all.

3 Though set on high, you look up - on the low - ly =
the proud you know with sor - row from a - far;
in all my trou - ble you are swift to save me,
and with your arm re - strain the threat of war.

4 For - ev - er you will keep your face to - wards us,
your truth, your faith - ful love – they will not cease:
then come in power, ful - fil your migh - ty pur - pose,
and grant to your cre - a - tion per - fect peace.

There is no moment

Maisemore 8 6 8 6 (CM)

Words: from Psalm 139
Brian Foley
Music: J Dykes Bower (1905–1981)

1 There is no mo - ment of___ my life,
2 Be - fore I speak,___ my words___ are known,
3 If I should close___ my eyes___ to him,
4 He knew my days___ be - fore___ all days,

no place where I___ may go, no___ ac - tion___ which___ God
and all that I___ de - cide. To___ come___ or___ go?___ God
he comes to give___ me sight; if___ I___ should go___ where
be - fore I came___ to be; he___ keeps___ me,___ loves___ me,

does___ not see,___ no thought he does not___ know.
knows___ my choice, and makes___ him - self my___ guide.
all___ is dark,___ he makes___ my dark - ness___ light.
in___ my ways ___ no lov - er such as___ he.

Alternative tune: Albano, *Hymns for Today's Church* 135

Words: From the *New Catholic Hymnal*
© 1971 Faber Music Ltd,
3 Queen Square, London WC1N 3AU

Music: © The executors of the late J Dykes Bower

Lord all-knowing

139B

Berkswell 8 7 8 7

Words: from Psalm 139
Christopher Idle
Music: English traditional melody
arranged David Iliff

1 Lord all-knowing, you have found me; every secret
2 Lord almighty, you have made me, fashioned me to
3 Lord all-holy, you have judged me by a standard

thought and word,___ all my actions,
keep your laws;___ your design and
true and right;___ all the best I

all my longings you have___ seen and you have___ heard.
your creation, every___ part of me is___ yours.
have to offer withers___ in your burning___ light.

4 Lord all-loving, you have saved me
in supreme and mighty grace;
by your Son's triumphant mercy,
suffering, dying in my place.

5 Lord all-glorious, you receive me
where your ransomed servants sing;
you have spoken, rescued, conquered –
Christ, our prophet, priest, and king!

Alternative tune: Cross of Jesus, *Hymns for Today's Church* 52

254

O Lord, come quickly

Bugeilio'r Gwenith Gwyn 8 7 8 7 D

IAMBIC

Words: from Psalm 141
Michael Perry
Music: Welsh traditional melody
arranged John Barnard

1 O Lord, come quick-ly when I call; re - ceive my prayer with fa - vour,_ fair
2 O Lord, I'll seek your dis - ci-pline – but streng-then me_ to choose it;_ your

as the even - ing sac - ri - fice, as in-cense sweet_ to sa - vour._ Keep
oil of grace a - noints my head – my head will not_ re - fuse it._ My

watch up - on my mouth, O Lord, and guard my lips from e - vil;_ so
eyes are fixed on you, O Lord, though dan-gers yet sur - round me;_ in

turn my heart from wick-ed ways that I may shame the de - vil._
life your love_ will be my rock, and death shall not con - found me._

Alternative tune: Dominus regit me, *Hymns for Today's Church* 44

142A

You are my refuge

Words: from Psalm 142
Michael Perry
Music: John Barnard

CHOIR

𝅘𝅥 = 104

mf

You are my re - fuge,

mf

I will praise your name; you are good to me, O __ Lord! __

f

ALL

3rd time **to Coda** ⊕

You are my re - fuge, I will praise your name; you are good to me, O __ Lord!

1 When I lift up my voice, and I
2 When I see no-one cares, and I
3 When he comes to my side and he

cry to the Lord, and I pour out my trou-bles be-fore him: I say
walk all a-lone, and my spi-rit grows wear-y with-in me:
an-swers my prayers, and he sets my soul free from its pri-son:

CODA

You are my re-fuge,

I will praise your name; you are good to me, O Lord!

rall.

257

143 A   Hear me, O Lord, in my distress

The Truth from above 8 8 8 8 (LM)

Words: from Psalm 143
David Preston
Music: English traditional melody
arranged R Vaughan Williams (1872–1958)

1 Hear me, O Lord,— in my dis-tress,— give
2 I claim no fav-our as of right;— you
3 My fierce op-press-or hunts me down = I

ear to my— des-pair-ing plea! In— faith-ful-ness,— in—
are the God— I serve and trust,— yet— judge me— not:— for—
shrink in dark-ness, like— the dead;— my— spi-rit— fails = all—

right-eous-ness,— oh,— hear my prayer_____ and ans-wer— me.
in your sight— no— liv-ing soul_____ is count-ed— just.
hope is gone,— my— heart is o - ver-whelmed with dread.

4 Days long since vanished I review,
I see the wonders of your hands,
and I stretch out my hands to you,
for you I thirst like desert sands.

5 Lord, answer me without delay!
I perish if you hide your face;
in you I trust: let this new day
bring word of your unfailing grace.

6 For your name's sake, Lord, hear my plea:
your servant's stricken life preserve!
From all oppression set me free
to live and love the God I serve.

Music arrangement: © Stainer & Bell Ltd,
82 High Road, London N2 9PW;
(USA) Galaxy Music Corporation,
131 West 86th Street, New York, NY 10016

Words: © David Preston/Jubilate Hymns †

To God our great salvation

145A

Crüger 7 6 7 6 D

Words: from Psalm 145
Timothy Dudley-Smith
Music: J Crüger (1598–1662)

1 To God our great sal – va – tion a tri-umph-song we raise,
with hymns of a – dor – a – tion and ev – er – last – ing praise.
That name be – yond all nam – ing, from age to age a – dored,
we lift on high, pro – claim – ing the great-ness of the Lord.

2 De – clare in song and sto – ry the won-ders we con – fess,
who hail the King of Glo – ry the Lord our Right-eous – ness.
In lov – ing – kind – ness car – ing his mer – cies stand dis – played,
for – giv – ing and for – bear – ing to all his hand has made.

3 His king-dom knows no end – ing, en – throned in light sub – lime,
his sov – ereign power ex – tend – ing be – yond all space and time.
To us and all things liv – ing he comes in word and deed,
for – bear – ing and for – giv – ing, to meet us in our need.

4 The King of all cre – a – tion is near to those who call;
the God of our sal – va – tion has stooped to save us all.
Lift high your hearts and voic – es, his prais – es sound a – gain;
in God his earth re – joic – es for ev – er-more. A – men!

I will exalt you O God

Words: from Psalm 145
from *The Liturgical Psalter*
David Frost and others
Music: T W Hanforth (1867–1948)

I will exalt you O ' God my ' king:
I will bless your ' name for ' ever · and ' ever.
Every ' day · will I ' bless you:
and praise your ' name for ' ever · and ' ever.

Great is the Lord *
and wonderfully ' worthy · to be ' praised:
his greatness is ' past ' searching ' out.
One generation shall praise your ' works · to an'other:
and de'clare your ' mighty ' acts.

Your kingdom is an ever'lasting ' kingdom:
and your dominion en'dures through ' all · gener'ations.
The Lord upholds all ' those who ' stumble:
and raises up ' those · that are ' bowed ' down.

The eyes of all look to ' you in ' hope:
and you give them their ' food in ' due ' season;
you open ' wide your ' hand:
and fill all things ' living · with your ' bounte·ous ' gift.

The Lord is just in ' all his ' ways:
and ' faithful · in ' all his ' dealings.
The Lord is near to all who ' call up'on him:
to all who ' call up'on him · in ' truth.

He will fulfil the desire of ' those that ' fear him:
he will ' hear their ' cry and ' save them.
The Lord preserves all ' those that ' love him:
but the wicked ' he will ' utterly · de'stroy.

Second part
My mouth shall speak the ' praises · of the ' Lord:
and let all flesh bless his holy ' name for ' ever · and ' ever.

Glory to the Father and ' to the ' Son:
and ' to the ' Holy ' Spirit;
as it was in the be'ginning · is ' now:
and shall be for ' ever. ' A'men.

Praise the God of our salvation

Canterbury Cathedral 8 7 8 7

Words: from Psalm 146
Timothy Dudley-Smith
Music: Alan Ridout

1 Praise the God of our sal - va - tion, all life long your
2 Turn to him, his help en - treat - ing; on - ly in his
3 Thank - ful hearts his praise have sound - ed down the a - ges

voi - ces raise! Stir your hearts to
mer - cy trust: hu - man pomp and
long gone by: hap - py they whose

a - dor - a - tion, set your souls to sing his praise!
power are fleet - ing; mor - tal flesh is born for dust.
hopes are found - ed in the God of earth and sky!

4 Faithful Lord of all things living –
by his bounty all are blessed,
bread to hungry bodies giving,
justice to the long-oppressed.

5 For the strength of our salvation,
light and life and length of days,
praise the King of all creation,
set your souls to sing his praise!

Alternative tune: Marching, *Hymns for Today's Church* 360

Music: © Alan Ridout

Words: © Timothy Dudley-Smith

147A   Fill your hearts with joy and gladness

Regent Square   8 7 8 7 8 7

Words: from Psalm 147
Timothy Dudley-Smith
Music: H T Smart (1813–1879)
verse 4 arranged with descant John Barnard

1 Fill your hearts with joy and glad-ness, sing and praise your God and mine!
2 Praise the Lord, his peo - ple, praise him! Wound-ed souls his com-fort know.
3 Praise the Lord for times and sea-sons, cloud and sun-shine, wind and rain;

Great the Lord in__ love and wis-dom, might and ma - jes - ty di - vine!
Those who fear him__ find his mer-cies, peace for pain and__ joy for woe;
spring to melt the__ snows of win - ter till the wa - ters__ flow a - gain;

He who framed the star - ry hea-vens knows and names them as they shine.
hum - ble hearts are high ex - alt - ed, hu - man pride and__ power laid low.
grass up - on the moun-tain pas-tures, gol - den val - leys__ thick with grain.

DESCANT

4 Fill your hearts with joy — and glad-ness, peace and plen-ty crown your days;

4 Fill your hearts with joy and glad-ness, peace and plen-ty crown your days;

love his laws, de - clare his judge-ments, walk in all — his — words and ways;

love his laws, de - clare his judge-ments, walk in all his — words and ways;

he the Lord and we his child - ren — praise the Lord, all — peo - ple, praise!

he the Lord and we his child-ren — praise the Lord, all peo-ple, praise!

147B(i)

O let the Church rejoice

Burgate 6 6 6 6 8 8

Words: from Psalm 147
Barbara Woollett
Music: Alan Ridout

1 O let the Church re - joice_____ in God our sav - iour's
2 Our God com-mands the storm_____ and sends the warm - ing_
3 He makes the mea - dow flower,_____ the clouds, the wind and_

grace,_____ for it is good to voice his all - de - serv - ing_ praise:
breeze;_____ he can with-in_ us form a life_ of joy_ and_ peace.
rain;_____ the hum-ble, by_ his power he'll lov - ing - ly_ sus - tain.

Sing al - le - lu - ia, praise the Lord – he builds his church and spreads his word!

4 The broken-hearted sigh –
   he bears their guilt and shame;
   like numbered stars on high
   he knows them all by name.
   Sing alleluia . . .

5 Hope in the Lord above –
   he will provide our needs;
   trust his unfailing love
   praise all his gracious deeds!
   Sing alleluia . . .

O let the Church rejoice

Christchurch 6 6 6 6 8 8

Words: from Psalm 147
Barbara Woollett
Music: C Steggall (1826–1905)

1 O   let   the Church re - joice   in   God   our   sav - iour's   grace,
2 Our God com-mands the   storm   and   sends the   warm - ing   breeze;
3 He   makes the mea - dow flower,   the   clouds, the   wind and   rain;

for   it   is good   to   voice   his   all - de - serv - ing   praise:
he   can with - in us   form   a   life of joy and   peace.
the   hum - ble, by his   power he'll lov - ing - ly sus - tain.

Sing   al - le - lu - ia,   praise the Lord – he   builds his church and spreads his word!

4 The broken-hearted sigh –
   he bears their guilt and shame;
   like numbered stars on high
   he knows them all by name.
    Sing alleluia . . .

5 Hope in the Lord above –
   he will provide our needs;
   trust his unfailing love,
   praise all his gracious deeds!
    Sing alleluia . . .

148A   Praise the Lord of heaven

Camberwell 6 5 6 5 D

Words: from Psalm 148
Timothy Dudley-Smith
Music: Michael Brierley

UNISON

1 Praise the Lord of hea - ven,   praise him in the height;
2 Earth and o - cean praise him;   moun-tains, hills and trees;
3 Now by prince and peo - ple   let his praise be told;

praise him, all his an - gels,   praise him, hosts of light.
fire and hail and tem-pest,   wind and storm and seas.
praise him, men and maid-ens,   praise him, young and old.

Sun and moon to - ge-ther,   shin-ing stars a - flame,   pla - nets in their
Praise him, fields and for-ests,   birds on flash-ing wings,   praise him, beasts and
He, the Lord of glo-ry!   We, his praise pro - claim!   High a - bove all

Fine after vv 1 and 2

cours-es, mag-ni - fy his name!
cat - tle, all cre - a - ted things.
hea-vens mag-ni - fy his name!

Alternative tune: Evelyns, *Hymns for Today's Church* 172

Music: © 1960 Josef Weinberger Ltd,
12–14 Mortimer Street, London W1N 7RD

1 Praise the Lord of hea-ven, praise him in the height;____
2 Earth and o-cean praise him; moun-tains, hills and trees;____
3 Now by prince and peo-ple let his praise be told;____

praise him, all his an-gels,__ praise him, hosts____ of__ light.
fire and hail and tem-pest,__ wind and storm____ and__ seas.
praise him, men and maid-ens,__ praise him, young____ and__ old.

Sun and moon to-ge-ther,__ shin-ing stars a-flame,____
Praise him, fields and for-ests,__ birds on flash-ing wings,____
He, the Lord of glo-ry!__ We, his praise pro-claim!____

Fine after vv 1 and 2

Organ interlude

pla-nets in their cours-es, mag-ni-fy his name!
praise him, beasts and cat-tle, all cre-a-ted things.
High a-bove all hea-vens mag-ni-fy his name!

The Unison and Harmony versions are harmonically compatible.

148B   Praise him, praise him, praise him

St Helens   12 13 13 10

Words: from Psalm 148
Michael Perry
Music: Kenneth W Coates
Descant: David Iliff

Alternative tune: Nicaea (adapted), *Hymns for Today's Church* 7

All things that are, praise God

Upton Scudamore 10 10 10 10

Words: from Psalm 148
Brian Foley
Music: John Barnard

1 All things that are, praise God by what they are — their be - ing
2 Praise God, all an - gels made by him to be _____ for ev - er
3 Praise God, all earth - ly things that he has made, _____ come, cold of

speaks to us of God who is; _____ so we may call on
in the ser - vice of his throne; _____ shine, sun and moon, all
win - ter, heat of sum - mer sun; _____ come, spring and au - tumn,

them to praise his name, _ to give with us the hon-our that is his.
stars whose light we see, _ and by your shin - ing make his great light known.
change and change a - gain, _ show in your chang-ing how his will is done.

4 Praise God, all lands and seas, all living things,
  all trees and plants that he has made to grow;
  all birds and beasts, praise, each in your own way,
  his greatness, which all things created show.

5 Praise God, all men and women, young and old –
  creation's highest praise is yours to sing;
  to honour God, to praise with every praise
  his Being, everywhere, in everything.

Alternative tune: Woodlands, *Hymns for Today's Church* 42

Music: © John Barnard/Jubilate Hymns †

Words: from the *New Catholic Hymnal*
© 1971 Faber Music Ltd,
3 Queen Square, London WC1N 3AU

Bring to the Lord a glad new song

Jerusalem 8 8 8 8 D (DLM)

Words: from Psalms 149 and 150
Michael Perry
Music: C H H Parry (1848–1918)

Slow but with animation

Bring to the Lord a glad new song, child-ren of grace ex-tol your king: your love and praise to God be - long - to in-stru-ments of mu - sic, *poco cresc.*

sing!   Let those be warned   who spurn God's name,   let rul - ers

all   o - bey God's word,   for jus - tice shall   bring ty - rants

poco rit.   **a tempo**

shame –   let ev-ery crea-ture praise the   Lord!

Praise the Lord with joyful cry

150A

Orientis partibus 7 7 7 7

Words: from Psalm 150
Fred Kaan
Music: P de Corbeil (died 1222)

1 Praise the Lord with joy - ful cry; let the mood of
2 Praise him with the sound that swings, with per - cus - sion,
3 Praise with life and voice the Lord, him who speaks in

praise run high. Praise him who with migh - ty deeds
brass and strings. Let the world at ev - ery chance
deed and word, who to life the world or - dained –

hu - man great - ness far ex - ceeds:___
praise him with a song and dance:___ Al - le - lu - ia!
let our praise be un - re - strained:

150B Let everything that has breath

Words: from Psalm 150
from *The Liturgical Psalter*
David Frost and others
Music: John Barnard

CHOIR Let ev-ery-thing that has breath

praise the Lord: ALL Let ev-ery-thing that has breath

praise the Lord! CHOIR O praise God in his sanc-tu-ary,

Words: From *The Psalms : A New Translation for Worship*
© English text 1976, 1977 David L Frost, John A Emerton,
Andrew A Macintosh, all rights reserved

praise him in the fir-ma-ment of his power; praise him for his migh-ty

acts,___ praise him ac - cord - ing to his a - bund - ant

good - ness:_____ ALL Let ev - ery-thing that___ has

breath___ praise_____ the Lord!

CHOIR Praise him in the blast of the ram's horn, praise him on the lute__ and harp, praise him with the tim-brels and dan - ces, praise him on the strings and pipe:_____ ALL Let ev-ery-thing that__ has breath praise_____ the Lord!

CHOIR Praise him on the high-sound-ing cym-bals, praise him on the loud____ cym-bals; let ev-ery-thing that____ has breath praise____ the Lord:____ ALL Let ev-ery-thing that____ has breath____ praise____ the Lord! CHOIR praise____ the Lord!

rit.

150C   O praise God in his sanctuary

Words: from Psalm 150
from *The Liturgical Psalter*
David Frost and others
Music: C V Stanford (1852–1924)

1 O praise God in his sanctua-ry: praise him in the firma-ment of his power.

2 Praise him for his migh-ty acts: praise him according to his a - bun-dant goodness.

3 Praise him in the blast of the ram's horn: praise him up - on the lute and harp.

4 Praise him with the timbrel and dan-ces: praise him up - on the strings and pipe.

TENORS AND BASSES

ff

5 Praise him on the high sounding cym-bals: praise him up - on the loud_ cymbals.

ALL VOICES   **HARMONY**

ff

6 Let everything that has breath praise the Lord: O praise___ the Lord.___

UNISON

Glory to the Father and to the Son:_ and to the Ho - ly Spirit;

HARMONY

as it was in the be-ginning is now: and shall be for ev-er. A - - - men.

151   O come let us sing out to the Lord

Words: from Psalms 95 and 96, *Venite*
from *The Liturgical Psalter*
David Frost and others

C V Stanford (1852–1924)

H Lawes (1595–1662)

1   O come let us sing ˈ out · to the ˈ Lord:
     let us shout in triumph to the ˈ rock of ˈ our salˈvation.
2   Let us come before his ˈ face with ˈ thanksgiving:
     and cry ˈ out to · him ˈ joyfully · in ˈ psalms.
3   For the Lord is a ˈ great ˈ God:
     and a great ˈ king a·bove ˈ all ˈ gods.
4   In his hand are the ˈ depths · of the ˈ earth:
     and the peaks of the ˈ mountains · are ˈ his ˈ also.

Second part
5   The sea is his and ˈ he ˈ made it:
     his hands ˈ moulded ˈ dry ˈ land.
6   Come let us worship and ˈ bow ˈ down:
     and kneel beˈfore the ˈ Lord our ˈ maker.
7   For he is the ˈ Lord our ˈ God:
     we are his ˈ people · and the ˈ sheep of · his ˈ pasture.
8   If only you would hear his ˈ voice toˈday:
     for he ˈ comes to ˈ judge the ˈ earth.
9   He shall judge the ˈ world with ˈ righteousness:
     and the ˈ peoples ˈ with his ˈ truth.

     Glory to the Father and ˈ to the ˈ Son:
     and ˈ to the ˈ Holy ˈ Spirit;
     as it was in the beˈginning · is ˈ now:
     and shall be for ˈ ever. ˈ Aˈmen.

Now lives the Lamb of God

Darwall's 148th 6 6 6 6 8 8

Words: from 1 Corinthians 5 and 15,
and Romans 6, *The Easter Anthems*
David Mowbray
Music: J Darwall (1731–1789)

1 Now lives the Lamb of God, our Pass-ov-er, the
2 Now ris-en from the dead Christ ne-ver dies a-
3 In A-dam all must die, for-lorn and un-for-
4 Give praise to God a-lone who life from death can

Christ, who once with nails and wood for us was
-gain; who in us, with Christ as head, sin ne-ver-
-given; in Christ we come a-live, the sec-ond
bring; whose migh-ty power can turn our win-ter

sac-ri-ficed:
-more shall reign:
Man from heaven. Come, keep the feast, the
in-to spring:

an-them sing that Christ in-deed is Lord and king!

Alternative tune: Harewood, *Hymns for Today's Church* 564

283

152B   Christ our passover

Words: from 1 Corinthians 5 and 15,
and Romans 6, *The Easter Anthems*
after *The Book of Common Prayer*
in *The Alternative Service Book 1980*

J Goss (1800–1880)

H Skeats (died 1831)

1   Christ our passover has been ᛁ sacri·ficed ᛁ for us:
so let us ᛁ cele'brate the ᛁ feast,

2   not with the old leaven of cor'ruption · and ᛁ wickedness:
but with the unleavened ᛁ bread of · sin'cerity · and ᛁ truth.

3   Christ once raised from the dead ᛁ dies no ᛁ more:
death has no ᛁ more do'minion ᛁ over him.

4   In dying he died to sin ᛁ once for ᛁ all:
in ᛁ living · he ᛁ lives to ᛁ God.

5   See yourselves therefore as ᛁ dead to ᛁ sin:
and alive to God in ᛁ Jesus ᛁ Christ our ᛁ Lord.

6   Christ has been ᛁ raised · from the ᛁ dead:
the ᛁ firstfruits · of ᛁ those who ᛁ sleep.

7   For as by ᛁ man came ᛁ death:
by man has come also the resur'rection ᛁ of the ᛁ dead;

8   for as in ᛁ Adam · all ᛁ die:
even so in Christ shall ᛁ all be ᛁ made a'live.

Glory to the Father and ᛁ to the ᛁ Son:
and ᛁ to the ᛁ Holy ᛁ Spirit;
as it was in the be'ginning · is ᛁ now:
and shall be for ᛁ ever. ᛁ A'men.

O bless the God of Israel

Morning Light 7 6 7 6 D

Words: from Luke 1,
The Song of Zechariah/Benedictus
Michael Perry
Music: G J Webb (1803–1887)

1 O bless the God of Is - rael, who comes to set us free,
2 Now from the house of Da - vid a child of grace is given;
3 Where once were fear and dark - ness the sun be - gins to rise –

who_ vi - sits and re - deems us and grants us li - ber - ty.
a_ Sav - iour comes a - mong us to raise us up to heaven.
the_ dawn - ing of for - give - ness up - on the sin - ner's eyes,

The pro - phets spoke of mer - cy, of_ res - cue and re - lease;_
Be - fore him goes the her - ald - fore - run - ner in the way,_
to guide the feet of pil - grims a - long the paths of peace:_

God_ shall ful - fil the pro - mise to bring our peo - ple peace.
the_ pro - phet of sal - va - tion, the mes - sen - ger of Day.
O_ bless our God and Sav - iour, with songs that ne - ver cease!

Alternative tune: Roewen, *Songs from the Psalms* 153A

153B(i) O praise our great and faithful God

Covenanters 8 6 8 6 (CM)

Words: from Luke 1,
The Song of Zechariah/Benedictus
Michael Hewlett
Music: American traditional melody

1 O praise our great and faithful God, the
2 The oath he swore to save us all he
3 O children's children, you in turn shall

God our parents knew, for in his Name the
kept, and it was done: pro - tec - tion, par - don,
go be - fore his face, to give the know - ledge

pro - phets spoke, and we have found them true.
peace and hope, we have them in his Son.
of his love and to pre - pare his ways.

4 Tell them the Dayspring from on high
has dawned for our release:
benighted, lost, in fear of death,
the world can know our peace.

5 To Father, Son and Spirit, praise!
To God whom we adore
be worship, glory, power and love,
both now and evermore!

286

O praise our great and faithful God 153B(ii)

Wiltshire 8 6 8 6 (CM)

Words: from Luke 1,
The Song of Zechariah/Benedictus
Michael Hewlett
Music: G T Smart (1776–1867)

1 O praise our great_ and faith - ful God,_ the
2 The oath he swore_ to save_ us all_ he
3 O child - ren's child - ren, you_ in turn_ shall

God_ our par - ents_ knew,_ for in_ his Name_ the
kept,_ and it_ was_ done:_ pro - tec - tion, par - don,
go_ be - fore_ his_ face, to give_ the know - ledge

pro - phets spoke, and_ we_____ have found_ them true.
peace_ and_ hope,_ we_ have_____ them in_ his_ Son.
of_ his_ love_ and_ to_____ pre - pare his_ ways.

4 Tcil them the Dayspring from on high
   has dawned for our release:
   benighted, lost, in fear of death,
   the world can know our peace.

5 To Father, Son and Spirit, praise!
   To God whom we adore
   be worship, glory, power and love,
   both now and evermore!

153c   Blessed be the Lord the God of Israel

Words: from Luke 1,
The Song of Zechariah/Benedictus
in *The Alternative Service Book 1980*
International Consultation on English Texts

J Turle (1802–1882)

G C Martin (1844–1916)

1   Blessed be the Lord the ⎜ God of ⎜ Israel:
for he has come to his ⎜ people · and ⎜ set them ⎜ free.
2   He has raised up for us a ⎜ mighty ⎜ saviour:
born of the ⎜ house · of his ⎜ servant ⎜ David.

3   Through his holy prophets he ⎜ promised · of ⎜ old:
that he would save us from our enemies
from the ⎜ hands of ⎜ all that ⎜ hate us.
4   He promised to show ⎜ mercy · to our ⎜ fathers:
and to re⎜member · his ⎜ holy ⎜ covenant.

5   This was the oath he swore to our ⎜ father ⎜ Abraham:
to set us ⎜ free · from the ⎜ hands of · our ⎜ enemies,
6   free to worship him with⎜out ⎜ fear:
holy and righteous in his sight ⎜ all the ⎜ days of · our ⎜ life.

7   You my child shall be called the prophet of the ⎜ Most ⎜ High:
for you will go before the ⎜ Lord · to pre⎜pare his ⎜ way,
8   to give his people knowledge ⎜ of sal⎜vation:
by the for⎜giveness · of ⎜ all their ⎜ sins.

9   In the tender compassion ⎜ of our ⎜ God:
the dawn from on ⎜ high shall ⎜ break up⎜on us,
10   to shine on those who dwell in darkness and the ⎜ shadow · of ⎜ death:
and to guide our feet ⎜ into · the ⎜ way of ⎜ peace.

Glory to the Father and ⎜ to the ⎜ Son:
and ⎜ to the ⎜ Holy ⎜ Spirit;
as it was in the be⎜ginning · is ⎜ now:
and shall be for ⎜ ever. ⎜ A⎜men.

Bless the Lord, created things

Antiphoner 7 7 7 6

Words: from *A Song of Creation/Benedicite*
Judy Davies
Music: Gradual, Paris 1685
arranged David Iliff

1 Bless the Lord, cre - a - ted things, high - est
2 Sun and moon and stars of heaven, show - ery
3 Scorch - ing wind and bit - ter cold, i - cy

hea - vens, an - gel host; bless the Fa - ther,
wa - ters, rain and dew, stor - my gale and
bliz - zard, morn - ing mist, light and dark - ness,

Spi - rit, Son: ____
fi - ery heat: ____ wor - ship, all cre - a - tion.
nights and days: ____

4 Frosty air and falling snow,
clouds and lightnings, dales and hills,
all that grows upon the earth:
worship, all creation.

5 Springs and rivers, ocean deeps,
whales and fishes of the sea,
prowling beasts and soaring birds:
worship, all creation.

6 All on earth who serve our God,
priests and people of the Lord,
upright, holy, humble hearts:
worship, all creation.

154B Angels, praise him

Little Barrington

Words: from *A Song of Creation*/*Benedicite*
Michael Perry
Music: John Barnard

UNISON

1 An-gels, praise him, hea-vens, praise him, wa-ters, praise him, Al - le -
2 Sun,— praise him, moon, praise him, stars,— praise him, Al - le -

-lu - ia! crea-tures of the Lord, all__ praise him for__
-lu - ia! showers, praise_ him, dews,— praise him for__

v 1

v 2

ev - er - more: ev - er - more:

3 Wind, praise him, fire,— praise him, heat, praise him, Al - le -
5 Earth, praise him, moun-tains, praise him, hills, praise him, Al - le -

Alternative tunes: Song of Creation or Angels, praise him, *Songs from the Psalms* 154B(i), 154B(ii)

-lu – ia! win – ter, praise him, sum-mer, praise him for__ ev – er –
-lu – ia! green things, praise him, wells,__ praise him for__ ev – er –

-more: 4 Nights, praise him, days, praise him, light, praise him, Al – le –
-more: 6 Seas, praise him, ri-vers, praise him, fish, praise him, Al – le –

-lu – ia! light-nings, praise him, clouds, praise him for__ ev – er – more:
-lu – ia! birds,__ praise him, beasts, praise him for__ ev – er – more:

7 Na – tions, praise him, church-es, praise him, saints, praise him, Al – le –

-lu – ia! all his peo – ple, join to praise him for__ ev – er – more!

154c — Bless the Lord all created things

Words: from *A Song of Creation/Benedicite*
after *The Book of Common Prayer*
in *The Alternative Service Book 1980*

P Whitlock (1903–1946)

C F South (1850–1916)

1 Bless the Lord all cre|ated | things:
 sing his | praise · and ex|alt him · for | ever.

2 Bless the | Lord you | heavens:
 sing his | praise · and ex|alt him · for | ever.

3 Bless the Lord you | angels · of the | Lord:
 bless the | Lord all | you his | hosts;

4 bless the Lord all | men · on the | earth:
 sing his | praise · and ex|alt him · for | ever.

5 O people of God | bless the | Lord:
 bless the | Lord you | priests · of the | Lord;

6 bless the Lord you | servants · of the | Lord:
 sing his | praise · and ex|alt him · for | ever.

7 Bless the Lord all men of | upright | spirit:
 bless the Lord you that are | holy · and | humble · in | heart.
 Bless the Father the Son and the | Holy | Spirit:
 sing his | praise · and ex|alt him · for | ever.

Great and wonderful your deeds

Württemberg 7 7 7 7 6

Words: from *Great and wonderful*
Christopher Idle
Music: *Hundert Arien* Dresden 1694

1 Great and won - der - ful your deeds, God from whom all
2 King of na - tions, take your crown! Ev - ery race shall
3 To the one al - migh - ty God, to the Lamb who

power pro - ceeds; true and right are all your ways –
soon bow down. Ho - ly God and Lord a - lone,
shed his blood, to the Spi - rit now be given

who shall not_ give thanks and praise? To your name be glo - ry!
jus - tice in_ your deeds is_ shown; all have seen your glo - ry.
by the hosts of earth and heaven love and praise and glo - ry!

155B   Wonderful your deeds, Lord

Erlestoke   6 5 6 5

Words: from *Great and wonderful*
David Mowbray
Music: John Barnard

1 Won-der-ful your deeds, Lord, just and true your ways;
2 Ho-ly is your name, Lord: fill our hearts with awe!
3 Na-tions bow in wor-ship, kneel-ing at your throne;
4 Praise to God the Fa-ther, praise to Christ the Lamb,

you are God al-migh-ty, king be-yond all praise.
Who shall not re-vere you now and ev-er-more?
faith-ful are your deal-ings, all your judge-ments known.
and to God the Spi-rit ev-er and a-men!

v 4

Alternative tune: North Coates, *Psalms for Today* 162B(ii), *Hymns for Today's Church* 384

Great and wonderful

Words: from *Great and wonderful*
derived from the Daily Office
of the Joint Liturgical Group

J Nares (1715–1783)

G J Elvey (1816–1893)

1   Great and wonderful are your deeds Lord ' God · the Al'mighty:
just and true are your ' ways O ' King · of the ' nations.

2   Who shall not revere and praise your ' name O ' Lord?
for ' you a'lone are ' holy.

3   All nations shall come and worship ' in your ' presence:
for your just ' dealings · have ' been re'vealed.

    To him who sits on the throne ' and · to the ' Lamb:
    be praise and honour   glory and might
    for ever and ' ever. ' A'men.

156A God of gods, we sound his praises

God of gods 8 7 8 7 8 8 8 7

Words: from *Te Deum*
Timothy Dudley-Smith
Music: Christian Strover

1 God of gods, we sound his prais - es, high-est heaven its ho - mage brings;
2 Christ-ians in their hearts en-throne him, tell his prais - es wide a - broad;
3 Hail the Christ, the King of glo - ry, he whose praise the an - gels cry;
4 Lord, we look for your re - turn-ing; teach us so to walk your ways,

earth and all cre - a - tion rais - es glo - ry to the King of kings:
pro-phets, priests, a - pos-tles own him mar-tyrs' crown and saints' re - ward.
born to share our hu - man sto - ry, love and la - bour, grieve and die:
hearts and minds your will dis - cern-ing, lives a - light with joy and praise:

ho - ly, ho - ly, ho - ly, name him, Lord of all his hosts pro-claim him;
Three-in - One his glo - ry shar-ing, earth and heaven his praise de - clar-ing,
by his cross his work com-plet - ed, sin - ners ran-somed, death de - feat-ed;
in your love and care en-fold us, by your con-stan - cy up-hold us;

to the ev - er - last - ing Fa - ther ev - ery tongue in tri - umph sings.
praise the high ma - jes - tic Fa - ther, praise the ev - er - last - ing Lord!
in the glo - ry of the Fa - ther Christ a - scend-ed reigns on high.
may your mer - cy, Lord and Fa - ther, keep us now and all our days!

God, we praise you

156B

Rustington 8 7 8 7 D

Words: from *Te Deum*
Christopher Idle
Music: C H H Parry (1848–1918)

1 God, we praise you! God, we bless you! God, we name you sove-reign Lord!
2 True a-pos-tles, faith-ful pro-phets, saints who set their world a-blaze,
3 Je-sus Christ, the king of glo-ry, ev-er-last-ing Son of God,
4 Christ, at God's right hand vic-tor-ious, you will judge the world you made;

Migh-ty King whom an-gels wor-ship, Fa-ther, by your church a-dored:
mar-tyrs, once un-known, un-heed-ed, join one grow-ing song of praise,
hum-ble was your vir-gin mo-ther, hard the lone-ly path you trod:
Lord, in mer-cy help your ser-vants for whose free-dom you have paid:

all cre-a-tion shows your glo-ry, heaven and earth draw near your throne
while your church on earth con-fess-es one ma-jes-tic Tri-ni-ty:
by your cross is sin de-feat-ed, hell con-front-ed face to face,
raise us up from dust to glo-ry, guard us from all sin to-day;

sing-ing 'Ho-ly, ho-ly, ho-ly, Lord of hosts, and God a-lone!'
Fa-ther, Son, and Ho-ly Spi-rit, God, our hope e-ter-nal-ly.
hea-ven o-pened to be-liev-ers, sin-ners jus-ti-fied by grace.
King en-throned a-bove all prais-es, save your peo-ple, God, we pray.

Alternative tune: Lux Eoi, *Psalms for Today* 115, *Hymns for Today's Church* 151

156c   You are God and we praise you

Words: *Te Deum*
in *The Alternative Service Book 1980*
International Consultation on English Texts

1   You are ˈ God · and we ˈ praise you:
    you are the ˈ Lord and ˈ we acˈclaim you;
2   you are the eˈternal ˈ Father:
    all creˈation ˈ worships ˈ you.

3   To you all angels *
    all the ˈ powers of ˈ heaven:
    cherubim and seraphim ˈ sing in ˈ endless ˈ praise,
4   Holy holy holy Lord *
    God of ˈ power and ˈ might:
    heaven and ˈ earth are ˈ full of · your ˈ glory.

5   The glorious company of aˈpostles ˈ praise you:
    the noble fellowship of prophets praise you
    the white-robed ˈ army · of ˈ martyrs ˈ praise you.
6   Throughout the world the holy ˈ Church acˈclaims you:
    Father of ˈ majesˈty unˈbounded;

Second part
7   your true and only Son *
    worthy of ˈ all ˈ worship:
    and the Holy ˈ Spirit ˈ advocate · and ˈ guide.

Verses *14–18* may be omitted.

H Smart (1813–1879)

B vv 8–13

W Hawes (1785–1846)

8 You Christ are the ˈ King of ˈ glory:
   the eˈternal ˈ Son · of the ˈ Father.
9 When you became man to ˈ set us ˈ free:
   you did not abˈhor the ˈ Virgin's ˈ womb.

10 You overcame the ˈ sting of ˈ death:
    and opened the kingdom of ˈ heaven · to ˈ all beˈlievers.
11 You are seated at God's right ˈ hand in ˈ glory:
    we believe that you will ˈ come and ˈ be our ˈ judge.

12 Come then Lord and ˈ help your ˈ people:
    bought with the ˈ price of ˈ your own ˈ blood;
13 and bring us ˈ with your ˈ saints:
    to ˈ glory ˈ everˈlasting.

A vv 14–18

J Turle (1802–1882)

B vv 14–18

R Woodward (1744–1777)

14 Save your people Lord and ˈ bless · your inˈheritance:
    govern and upˈhold them ˈ now and ˈ always.
15 Day by ˈ day we ˈ bless you:
    we ˈ praise your ˈ name for ˈ ever.

16 Keep us today Lord from ˈ all ˈ sin:
    have mercy ˈ on us ˈ Lord have ˈ mercy.
17 Lord show us your ˈ love and ˈ mercy:
    for we ˈ put our ˈ trust in ˈ you.

Second part
18 In you Lord ˈ is our ˈ hope:
    let us not be conˈfounded ˈ at the ˈ last.

156D(i) Great is the Lord we now acclaim

Acclamation 8 8 8 8 (LM)

Words: from *Te Deum*
David Mowbray
Music: Andrew Maries

1 Great is the Lord we now ac-claim — God ev-er-last-ing is — his name: let heaven and earth with mu-sic ring, — and 'Ho-ly, ho-ly, ho-ly' sing!

2 Let pro-phets and — a-pos-tles join — with mar-tyrs in — tri-um-phant line — to e-cho the an-gel-ic cry — and ce-le-brate God's mys-te-ry.

3 We praise God's true — and on-ly Son, for ev-er with — the Fa-ther one; — we praise the Spi-rit at — their side, the Chur-ch's ad-vo-cate and guide.

This simpler rhythm may be substituted for bars 3 and 4:

God ev-er-last-ing is his name: let

4 When once the time had fully come
Christ did not scorn the Virgin's womb;
our Lord the sting of death defied
and flung the gate of heaven wide!

5 He shed his blood to pay sin's price,
the full and perfect sacrifice;
as Saviour, reigns eternally,
as Judge of all, presides on high.

6 Lord God, protect us all from sin,
our hearts to love and goodness win;
that we yet firm in faith, shall stay
unshaken in the last great day.

Great is the Lord we now acclaim 156D(ii)

Old 100th 8 8 8 8 (LM)

Words: from *Te Deum*
David Mowbray
Music: melody from *Genevan Psalter* 1551

1 Great is the Lord we now ac - claim — God
2 Let pro - phets and a - pos - tles join with
3 We praise God's true and on - ly Son, for

ev - er - last - ing is his name: let heaven and earth with
mar - tyrs in tri - umph - ant line to e - cho the an -
ev - er with the Fa - ther one; we praise the Spi - rit

mu - sic ring, and 'Ho - ly, ho - ly, ho - ly' sing!
- gel - ic cry and ce - le - brate God's mys - te - ry.
at their side, the Chur-ch's ad - vo - cate___ and guide.

4 When once the time had fully come
 Christ did not scorn the Virgin's womb;
 our Lord the sting of death defied
 and flung the gate of heaven wide!

5 He shed his blood to pay sin's price,
 the full and perfect sacrifice;
 as Saviour, reigns eternally,
 as Judge of all, presides on high.

6 Lord God, protect us all from sin,
 our hearts to love and goodness win;
 that we yet firm in faith, shall stay
 unshaken in the last great day.

157A All glory be to God

Nicolaus 8 6 8 8 6

Words: from *Gloria in excelsis*
Timothy Dudley-Smith
Music: Nicolaus Herman (c1485–1561)
arranged J S Bach (1685–1750)

1 All glo-ry be to God on high, his peace on earth pro-claim; to all his peo-ple tell a-broad the grace and glo-ry of the Lord, and bless his ho-ly name.

2 In songs of thank-ful-ness and praise our hearts their hom-age bring to wor-ship him who reigns a-bove, al-migh-ty Fa-ther, Lord of love, our God and hea-venly King.

3 O Christ, the Fa-ther's on-ly Son, O Lamb en-throned on high, O Je-sus, who for sin-ners died and reigns at God the Fa-ther's side, in mer-cy hear our cry.

4 Most high and ho-ly is the Lord, most high his hea-venly throne; where God the Fa-ther, God the Son, and God the Spi-rit, ev-er One, in glo-ry reigns a-lone.

Glory to God in the highest

Words: from *Gloria in excelsis*
in *The Alternative Service Book 1980*
International Consultation on English Texts

F A G Ouseley (1825–1889)

W H Havergal (1793–1870)

1 Glory to ⸍ God · in the ⸍ highest:
 and ⸍ peace · to his ⸍ people · on ⸍ earth.

2 Lord God ⸍ heaven·ly ⸍ King:
 al⸍mighty ⸍ God and ⸍ Father,

3 we worship you we ⸍ give you ⸍ thanks:
 we ⸍ praise you ⸍ for your ⸍ glory.

4 Lord Jesus Christ only ⸍ Son · of the ⸍ Father:
 Lord ⸍ God ⸍ Lamb of ⸍ God,

5 you take away the ⸍ sin · of the ⸍ world:
 have ⸍ mercy ⸍ on ⸍ us;

6 you are seated at the right hand ⸍ of the ⸍ Father:
 re⸍ceive ⸍ our ⸍ prayer.

7 For you a⸍lone · are the ⸍ Holy One:
 you a⸍lone ⸍ are the ⸍ Lord,

8 you alone are the Most High
 Jesus Christ with the ⸍ Holy ⸍ Spirit:
 in the glory of God the ⸍ Father. ⸍ A⸍men.

158A(i) Saviour Christ, in mercy come

Salvator mundi 7 7 7 7

Words: from *Saviour of the world*
David Mowbray and Michael Perry
Music: David Llewellyn Green

1 Sav - iour Christ, in__ mer - cy come! By your cross_ and
2 Come in power and__ loose our chains, come in peace, for -
3 Come to live a - mong us, Lord – come to save_ us

life__ laid down__ set__ your__ wait - ing__
- give__ our sins,__ come__ in__ truth__ to__
by__ your word;__ come__ to - day__ and__

peo - ple__ free =__ come a - mong us,__ Lord, to - day:
make us__ wise,__ come and__ fill__ our__ hearts with praise:
make us__ one,__ Sav - iour_ Christ, in__ mer - cy__ come!

Saviour Christ, in mercy come 158A(ii)

Culbach 7 7 7 7

Words: from *Saviour of the world*
David Mowbray and Michael Perry
Music: adapted from a chorale in J Scheffler's
Heilige Seelenlust Breslau 1657

1 Sav - iour Christ, in mer - cy come! By your cross and
2 Come in power and loose our chains, come in peace, for -
3 Come to live a - mong us, Lord – come to save us

life laid____ down set your wait - ing
- give our____ sins, come in truth to
by your____ word; come to - day and

peo - ple free – come a - mong us, Lord, to - day:
make us wise, come and fill our hearts with__ praise:
make us one, Sav - iour Christ, in mer - cy__ come!

158B   Jesus, Saviour of the world

St Albinus 7 8 7 8 4

Words: from *Saviour of the world*
Christopher Idle
Music: H J Gauntlett (1805–1876)

1 Je - sus, Sav - iour of the world, you have bought your
2 Christ, who once on Ga - li - lee came to your dis -
3 Lord, make known your pro - mised power; show your - self our
4 When you come, Lord Je - sus Christ, fill - ing earth and

peo - ple's_ free - dom by your cross, your life laid_ down:
-ci - ples'_ res - cue: we, like them, cry out for_ help –
strong de - liv - erer: so our prayer shall turn to_ praise –
heaven with_ won - der, come to make us one with_ you –

now bring in your glo - rious king - dom. Come to help us!
free us from our sins, we ask you. Come to save us!
hear us, stay with us for ev - er. Come to rule us!
heirs of life, to reign in splen - dour. Al - le - lu - ia!

Saviour of the world

Words: *Saviour of the world*
derived from the Daily Office
of the Joint Liturgical Group

Roger Lowman

P C Buck (1871–1947)

1 Jesus saviour of the world *
   come to us ' in your ' mercy:
   we look to ' you to ' save and ' help us.
2 By your cross and your life laid down
   you set your ' people ' free:
   we look to ' you to ' save and ' help us.

3 When they were ready to perish you ' saved · your dis'ciples:
   we look to ' you to ' come to · our ' help.
4 In the greatness of your mercy loose us ' from our ' chains:
   forgive the ' sins of ' all your ' people.

5 Make yourself known as our saviour and ' mighty · de'liverer:
   save and ' help us · that ' we may ' praise you.
6 Come now and dwell with us ' Lord Christ ' Jesus:
   hear our ' prayer · and be ' with us ' always.

Second part
7 And when you ' come in · your ' glory:
   make us to be one with you *
   and to ' share the ' life of · your ' kingdom.

159A   Light of gladness, Lord of glory

Quem pastores laudavere   8 8 8 7

Words: from *Phos hilaron*
Christopher Idle
Music: fourteenth-century German melody
arranged John Barnard

1 Light of glad - ness, Lord of glo - ry, Je - sus
2 Let us sing at sun's de - scend - ing as we
3 Son of God, through all the a - ges wor - thy

Christ our king most ho - ly, shine a - mong us
see the lights of even - ing, Fa - ther, Son, and
of our ho - liest prais - es, yours the life that

in your mer - cy: earth and hea - ven join their hymn.
Spi - rit prais - ing with the ho - ly se - ra - phim.
ne - ver ceas - es, light which ne - ver shall grow dim.

Light of gladness, shining radiance 159B

Light of gladness 8 7 8 7

Words: from *Phos hilaron*
Words and music: Paul Inwood

1 Light of glad - ness, shin - ing rad - iance of___ the hea - venly
2 As the day___ draws near its end - ing, sun - light dims___ with
3 Son of God,___ the world's re - deem - er, end - less prais - es

Fa - ther's face:_____ Je - sus Christ,___ we
fad - ing rays,_____ to the Fa - ther,
are_____ your due:_____ Lord of life,___ let

greet you, bless___ you, ho - ly Lord of sav - ing grace.
Son and Spi - rit now___ we sing our song___ of praise.
all cre - a - tion bring___ its joy - ful thanks to you.

Alternative tunes: Shipston, Halton Holgate, *Hymns for Today's Church* 282, 370

Words and music: © Paul Inwood/Magnificat Music,
St Thomas More Centre, The Burroughs, Hendon, London NW4 4TY;
(USA) OCP Publications, 5536 NE Hassalo, Portland, Oregon 97213, USA

159C   O gladdening light

Nunc dimittis   6 6 7 D

Words: from *Phos hilaron*
R S Bridges (1844–1930)
in this version Word & Music
Music: from *The Genevan Psalter* 1549
arranged C Goudimel (c1514–1572)

1 O glad-dening light,— O grace of God the Fa-ther's
2 As day fades in - to night we see the eve - ning
3 To you of right— be - longs the praise of all our

face, the e - ter-nal splen-dour wear - ing: ce - les-tial, ho - ly,
light, our hymn of love out - pour - ing; Fa - ther of might un -
songs, O Son of God, life - giv - er; you, there-fore, Lord most

blessed, our sav - iour Je - sus Christ, joy - ful in your ap - pear - ing.
-known, you, his in - car-nate Son, and Spi - rit blessed a - dor - ing.
high, the world shall glo - ri - fy and shall ex - alt for ev - er.

Alternative tune: *Songs from the Psalms* 159C

My soul proclaims the greatness of the Lord   160A

Andrew Mark

Words: from Luke 1,
The Song of Mary/Magnificat
Christopher Idle
Music: Norman Warren

1 My soul pro-claims the great-ness of the Lord, and my
2 In ev-ery age, for those who fear the Lord come his
3 To Is-ra-el his ser-vant he brings help, and the

spi-rit sings for joy to my sav-iour God! His
mer-cy, and the strength of his migh-ty arm; he
pro-mise to our fa-thers is now ful-filled: for

low-ly slave he looked up-on in love: they will call me hap-py now, for
routs the proud, throws mon-archs off their thrones, while he lifts the low-ly high, fills
Christ has come ac-cord-ing to his word, and the mer-cy that he showed to

migh-ty are the works he has done, and ho-ly is his name!
hun-gry souls with food, and the rich sends emp-ty a-way.
A-bra-ham is now for his child-ren's child-ren ev-er-more.

v 3

311

160B With Mary let my soul rejoice

St Stephen 8 6 8 6 (CM)

Words: from Luke 1,
The Song of Mary/Magnificat
David Mowbray
Music: W Jones (1726–1800)

1 With Ma - ry let my＿ soul re - joice, and＿
2 How strong his arm, how＿ great his power! The＿
3 The rich our God will＿ send a - way and＿

praise God's＿ ho - ly name – his sav - ing love from
proud he＿ will dis - own; the meek and hum - ble
feed the＿ hun - gry poor; the arms of love re -

first＿ to＿ last, from age to＿ age, the＿ same!
he＿ ex - alts to share his＿ glo - rious＿ throne.
-main out - stretched at mer - cy's＿ o - pen＿ door.

4 So shall God's promise be fulfilled,
  to Israel firmly made:
  a child is born, a Son is given
  whose crown will never fade.

5 All glory to the Father, Son
  and Spirit now proclaim;
  with Mary let the world rejoice
  and praise God's holy name!

My soul proclaims

Words: from Luke 1,
The Song of Mary/Magnificat
in *The Alternative Service Book 1980*
International Consultation on English Texts

E J Hopkins (1818–1901)

Andrew Millington

1 My soul proclaims the ' greatness · of the ' Lord:
my spirit re'joices · in ' God my ' saviour;
2 for he has looked with favour on his ' lowly ' servant:
from this day all gener'ations · will ' call me ' blessed;

Second part

3 the Almighty has done ' great things ' for me:
and ' holy ' is his ' name.

4 He has mercy on ' those who ' fear him:
in ' every ' gener'ation.

5 He has shown the ' strength · of his ' arm:
he has scattered the ' proud in ' their con'ceit.

6 He has cast down the mighty ' from their ' thrones:
and has ' lifted ' up the ' lowly.
7 He has filled the hungry with ' good ' things:
and the rich he has ' sent a'way ' empty.

8 He has come to the help of his ' servant ' Israel:
for he has re'membered · his ' promise · of ' mercy,
9 the promise he ' made · to our ' fathers:
to Abraham ' and his ' children · for ' ever.

Glory to the Father and ' to the ' Son:
and ' to the ' Holy ' Spirit;
as it was in the be'ginning · is ' now:
and shall be for ' ever. ' A'men.

161A Bless the Lord, our fathers' God

Orientis partibus 7 7 7 7

Words: from *Bless the Lord*
Christopher Idle
Music: P de Corbeil (died 1222)

1 Bless the Lord, our fa - thers' God,
2 Bless the Lord who reigns on high
3 Bless the Lord for ev - er - more,

bless the name of___ hea - ven's king; bless him in his
throned a - bove the___ che - ru - bim; bless the Lord who
bless the Ho - ly___ Tri - ni - ty; bless the Fa - ther,

ho - ly___ place, tell his praise, his glo - ries sing.
knows the___ depths, show his praise and wor - ship him.
Spi - rit,___ Son, sing his praise e - ter - nal - ly!

Bless the Lord the God of our fathers 161B(i)

Words: *Bless the Lord*
derived from the Daily Office
of the Joint Liturgical Group
Music: John Barnard

CHOIR
1 Bless the Lord the God of our fa - thers: sing his

praise and ex - alt him for ev - er. 2 Bless his ho - ly and
ALL
CHOIR

glo - ri - ous name: sing his praise and ex - alt him for ev - er.
ALL

CHOIR
3 Bless him in his ho - ly and glo - ri - ous tem - ple: sing his
ALL

This setting may be sung in harmony or in unison, with or without accompaniment.

praise and ex - alt him for ev - er. 4 Bless___ him

who___ be - holds___ the depths: **sing___ his praise and ex -**

- alt him for ev - er. 5 Bless him who sits___ be - tween___ the

che - ru - bim: **sing___ his praise and ex - alt him for**

ev - er. 6 Bless___ him on___ the throne of his king - dom:

CHOIR

ALL

CHOIR

ALL

CHOIR

ALL
sing— his praise and ex - alt him for ev - er.

CHOIR
7 Bless— him in— the heights of hea - ven: ALL sing— his

praise and ex - alt him for ev - er. CHOIR 8 Bless— the

Fa - ther, the Son and the Ho - ly Spi - rit:

poco rall.
ALL
sing— his praise and ex - alt him for ev - er.

161B(ii) Bless the Lord the God of our fathers

Words: *Bless the Lord*
derived from the Daily Office
of the Joint Liturgical Group
Music: Norman Warren

Brightly

UNISON

LEADER
1 Bless the Lord the

God of our fa - thers: **sing his praise and ex - alt him for ev - er.**

LEADER
2 Bless his ho - ly and glo - rious name:

ALL
sing his praise and ex -

- alt him for ev - er. 3 Bless him in his ho - ly and glo - rious tem - ple:

Alternative tune: *Songs from the Psalms* 161B

6 Bless him on the ___ throne of his king - dom: sing his praise and ex -

- alt him for ev - er. 7 Bless him in the heights of hea - ven:

sing his praise and ex - alt him for ev - er. 8 Bless the Fa - ther, the

Son and the Ho - ly Spi - rit: sing his praise and ex - alt him for ev - er.

Bless the Lord the God of our fathers 161C

Words: *Bless the Lord*
derived from the Daily Office
of the Joint Liturgical Group

A

G C Martin (1844–1916)

B

George Guest

1 Bless the Lord the ' God of · our ' fathers:
   sing his ' praise · and ex'alt him · for ' ever.
2 Bless his holy and ' glori·ous ' name:
   sing his ' praise · and ex'alt him · for ' ever.

3 Bless him in his holy and ' glori·ous ' temple:
   sing his ' praise · and ex'alt him · for ' ever.
4 Bless him who be'holds the ' depths:
   sing his ' praise · and ex'alt him · for ' ever.

5 Bless him who sits be'tween the ' cherubim:
   sing his ' praise · and ex'alt him · for ' ever.
6 Bless him on the ' throne of · his ' kingdom:
   sing his ' praise · and ex'alt him · for ' ever.

7 Bless him in the ' heights of ' heaven:
   sing his ' praise · and ex'alt him · for ' ever.
8 Bless the Father the Son and the ' Holy ' Spirit:
   sing his ' praise · and ex'alt him · for ' ever.

162 A

Faithful vigil ended

Faithful vigil 6 5 6 5

Words: from Luke 2,
The Song of Simeon/Nunc dimittis
Timothy Dudley-Smith
Music: David Wilson
arranged John Barnard

1 Faith - ful vi - gil end - ed, watch-ing, wait - ing cease:
2 All the Spi - rit pro - mised, all the Fa - ther willed,
3 This your great de - liver - ance sets your peo - ple free;
4 Christ, your peo-ple's glo - ry! watch-ing, doubt-ing cease:

Mas - ter, grant your ser - vant his dis-charge in peace.
now these eyes be - hold it per - fect-ly ful - filled.
Christ their light up - lift - ed all the na - tions see.
grant to us your ser - vants our dis-charge in peace.

Alternative tune: Caswall, *Hymns for Today's Church* 126

Lord, now let your servant

Oakmount 6 5 6 5

Words: from Luke 2,
The Song of Simeon/Nunc dimittis
J E Seddon (1915–1983)
Music: Hugh Benham

1 Lord, now let your ser - vant go his way in peace –
2 For my eyes have seen him pro-mised from of old –
3 Light of re - ve - la - tion to the gen - tiles shown,

your great love has brought me joy that will not cease:
sav - iour of all peo - ple, shep - herd of one fold:
light of Is - rael's glo - ry to the world made known.

162B(ii)   Lord, now let your servant

North Coates   6 5 6 5

Words: from Luke 2,
The Song of Simeon/Nunc dimittis
J E Seddon (1915–1983)
Music: T R Matthews (1826–1910)

1 Lord, now let your ser - vant go his way in peace –
2 For my eyes have seen him pro - mised from of old –
3 Light of re - ve - la - tion to the gen - tiles shown,

your great love has brought me joy that will not cease:
sav - iour of all peo - ple, shep - herd of one fold:
light of Is - rael's glo - ry to the world made known.

Lord now you let your servant

Words: from Luke 2,
The Song of Simeon/Nunc dimittis
in *The Alternative Service Book 1980*
International Consultation on English Texts

G A Macfarren (1813–1887)

J Battishill (1738–1801)

1 Lord now you let your servant ' go in ' peace:
your ' word has ' been ful'filled.

2 My own eyes have ' seen the · sal'vation:
which you have prepared in the ' sight of ' every ' people;

3 a light to re'veal you · to the ' nations:
and the ' glory · of your ' people ' Israel.

Glory to the Father and ' to the ' Son:
and ' to the ' Holy ' Spirit;
as it was in the be'ginning · is ' now:
and shall be for ' ever. ' A'men.

162D Now at last

Bertem 3 8 3 6

Words: from Luke 2,
The Song of Simeon/Nunc dimittis
Michael Saward
Music: David Iliff

UNISON

1 Now at last your ser - vant can de - part in peace,
2 My own eyes have wit - nessed your sal - va - tion, Lord,
3 Light for all, re - veal - ing you to ev - ery land;
4 Prais - es be to God the Fa - ther, Spi - rit, Son —

last verse only
for a few voices

for your word is fi - nal - ly ful - filled:
which is seen through - out the wait - ing world,
glo - rious sight, your peo - ple Is - rael's hope.
Three - in - One, the God whom we a - dore!

All praise to Christ

Engelberg   10 10 10 4

Words: from Philippians 2,
The Song of Christ's Glory
F B Tucker (1895–1984)
Music: C V Stanford (1852–1924)

1 All praise to Christ, our Lord and king di-vine,_____ yield-ing your
2 You came to us in low-li-ness of thought;_____ by you the
3 The mind of Christ is as our mind should be —_____ he was a

glo - ry in your love's de - sign,_____ that in our dark-ened hearts your
out - cast and the poor were sought,_____ and by your death was our re-
ser - vant, that we might be free;_____ humb-ling him - self to death on

grace might shine:_____ Al - le - lu - ia!
-demp - tion bought:_____ Al - le - lu - ia!
Cal - va - ry:_____

all a - dored:_____ Al - le - lu - ia! A - men.

4 And so we see in God's great purpose, how
   Christ has been raised above all creatures now;
   and at his name shall every nation bow:
      Alleluia!

5 Let every tongue confess with one accord,
   in heaven and earth, that Jesus Christ is Lord,
   and God the Father be by all adored:
      Alleluia! (Amen.)

Alternative tune: Creation, *Hymns for Today's Church* 204

163B Before the heaven and earth

Narenza 6 6 8 6 (SM)

Words: from Philippians 2, *The Song of Christ's Glory*
Brian Black and Word & Music
Music: from J Leisentritt, *Catholicum Hymnologium* 1584
arranged W H Havergal (1793–1870)
verse 6 arranged with descant John Barnard

1 Be - fore the heaven and earth were
2 Though in the form of God and
3 From heights of heaven he came to
4 The Son be - came true Man and
5 O - be - dient to his death – that

made by God's de - cree, the Son of God all -
rich be - yond com - pare, he did not think to
this world full of sin, to meet with hun - ger,
took a ser - vant's role; with low - li - ness and
death up - on a cross, no son had ev - er

- glo - rious dwelt in God's e - ter - ni - ty.
grasp his prize; nor did he lin - ger there.
ha - tred, hell – our life, our love to win.
self - less love he came, to make us whole.
shown such love, nor fa - ther known such loss.

Alternative tune: *Songs from the Psalms* 163B

DESCANT
6 To him en-throned on high, by____

UNISON
6 To him en-throned on high, by

an-gel hosts a-dored,____ all knees shall bow, and

an-gel hosts a-dored, all knees shall bow, and

tongues con-fess that____ Je-sus Christ is Lord.

tongues con-fess that Je-sus Christ is Lord.

163c   Christ Jesus was in the form of God

Words: from Philippians 2,
The Song of Christ's Glory
Liturgy of the Church of South Africa

E J Hopkins (1818–1901)

John Barnard

1   Christ Jesus was in the | form of | God:
    but he did not | cling · to e|quality · with | God.
2   He emptied himself *****
    taking the | form · of a | servant:
    and was | born · in the | likeness · of | men.

3   Being found in human form he | humbled · him|self:
    and became obedient unto death | even | death · on a | cross.
4   Therefore God has | highly · ex|alted him:
    and bestowed on him the | name a·bove | every | name,

5   that at the name of Jesus every | knee should | bow:
    in heaven and on | earth and | under · the | earth;
6   and every tongue confess that Jesus | Christ is | Lord:
    to the | glory · of | God the | Father.

    Glory to the Father and | to the | Son:
    and | to the | Holy | Spirit;
    as it was in the be|ginning · is | now:
    and shall be for | ever. | A|men.

A setting for choir is available in *Church Family Worship* 800.

Though Christ put on our frail humanity 163D

Sursum Corda   10 10 10 10

Words: from Philippians 2,
The Song of Christ's Glory
Stephen Horsfall
Music: A M Smith (1879–1971)

1 Though Christ put on our frail hu-man-i - ty,   he
2 As God and man he chose the way to death,   bear-
3 Since for our sake he glad-ly went to die,   tak-
4 So at the name of Je-sus, ev-ery knee   in

was in ve-ry truth our God and king;   and yet he did not
-ing our sins up-on the cru-el cross;   he blessed his kil-lers
-ing up-on him-self our ra-ce's shame,   God raised him, and ex-
heaven, on earth and in the depths, should bow;   and ev-ery tongue con-

claim e-qual-i - ty,   but trod the path of hum-ble suf-fer - ing.
with his dy-ing breath,   his a - go-ny re-deemed our griev-ous loss.
-alt-ed him on high,   gave him the high-est place and ho-liest name:
-fess that on-ly he   is Lord. Come, let us praise his glo-ry now!

164A   Heavenly hosts in ceaseless worship

Blaenwern   8 7 8 7 D

Words: from Revelation 4, 5,
Glory and honour
Timothy Dudley-Smith
Music: W P Rowlands (1860–1937)

1 Hea - venly hosts in cease - less wor - ship
2 All cre - a - tion, all___ re - demp - tion,

'Ho - ly, ho - ly, ho - ly!' cry;
join___ to sing the sav - iour's worth;

'He who is, who was___ and will be,
Lamb of God whose blood___ has bought us,

God al - migh - ty, Lord most___ high.'
kings and priests,___ to reign on___ earth.

Alternative tune: Gott Will's machen, *Psalms for Today* 100A(ii), *Hymns for Today's Church* 360

Praise and hon - our, power__ and glo - ry,
Wealth and wis - dom, power__ and glo - ry,

be to him__ who reigns__ a - lone!
hon - our, might,__ do - min - ion,__ praise,

We, with all his hands__ have fash - ioned,
now be his from all__ his crea - tures

fall__ be - fore__ the Fa - ther's__ throne.
and__ to ev - er - last - ing__ days!

164B   Glory and honour

Schönster Herr Jesu   5 5 9 5 5 8

Words: from Revelation 4, 5,
Glory and honour
Michael Perry
Music: *Silesian Folk Songs* Leipzig 1842

1 Glo - ry and hon - our, wis - dom and splen - dour,
2 Once was the ran - som paid for our free - dom—

Lord of cre - a - tion, are yours a - lone:
from ev - ery na - tion with you we reign:

all of earth's crea - tures in ex - ul - ta - tion
yours be the prais - es, high ve - ne - ra - tion,

sing to the Lamb up - on the throne.
wor - ship for ev - er - more. A - men.

Glory and honour

Words: from Revelation 4, 5,
Glory and honour
derived from the Daily Office
of the Joint Liturgical Group

G R Woodward (1848–1934)

J Hindle (1761–1796)

1 Glory and ˈ honour · and ˈ power:
are yours by ˈ right O ˈ Lord our ˈ God:

2 for you creˈated ˈ all things:
and by your ˈ will they ˈ have their ˈ being.

3 Glory and ˈ honour · and ˈ power:
are yours by ˈ right O ˈ Lamb · who was ˈ slain;

4 for by your blood you ransomed ˈ us for ˈ God:
from every race and language *
from ˈ every ˈ people · and ˈ nation,

5 to make us a ˈ kingdom · of ˈ priests:
to stand and ˈ serve beˈfore our ˈ God.

To him who sits on the throne ˈ and · to the ˈ Lamb:
be praise and honour glory and might *
for ever and ˈ ever. ˈ Aˈmen.

165A(i) Before the ending of the day

Alicia 8 8 8 8 (LM)

Words: from *Te Lucis ante terminum*
(Before the ending of the day)
in this version Jubilate Hymns
Music: Andrew Maries

Gently rocking like a lullaby

1 Be-fore the end - ing   of___ the day,
2 Bless us in sleep, that we___ may find
3 O Fa-ther, may your will__ be done

Cre - a - tor of the world, we pray: pro - tect__ us by your migh-ty grace,
no ter-rors to dis - turb_ our mind; our cun - ning e - ne - my_ re-strain –
through Je-sus Christ your on - ly Son; whom with_ the Spi - rit we_ a-dore,

grant us your mer   -   cy and__ your peace:_____
guard us from sin_____ and all__ its stain._____
one God, both now_____ and ev - er - more._____

(Fine)

Before the ending of the day 165A(ii)

Tallis' Canon 8 8 8 8 (LM)

Words: from *Te Lucis ante terminum*
(Before the ending of the day)
in this version Jubilate Hymns
Music: T Tallis (c1505–1585)

1 Be - fore the end - ing of the day, Cre -
2 Bless us in sleep, that we may find no
3 O Fa - ther, may your will be done through

-a - tor of the world, we pray: pro - tect us by your
ter - rors to dis - turb our mind; our cun - ning e - ne -
Je - sus Christ your on - ly Son; whom with the Spi - rit

migh - ty grace, grant us your mer - cy and your peace:
-my re - strain – guard us from sin and all its stain.
we a - dore, one God, both now and ev - er - more.

165B(i)   Now evening comes

Charnwood   8 6 8 6 (CM)

Words: from *Te Lucis ante terminum*
(Before the ending of the day)
Michael Perry
Music: Peter White

UNISON

1 Now even - ing comes to close the day, and soon the
2 In - to your hands, e - ter - nal Friend, we give our -
3 In wak - ing, lift our thoughts a - bove, in sleep - ing,
4 To Fa - ther, Son and Spi - rit — praise, all mor - tal

si - lent hours shall ban - ish all our fears a -
- selves a - gain, and to your watch - ful care com -
guard us still, that we may rise to know your
praise be given, till sleep at last shall end our

- way, and sleep re - new our powers.
- mend all those in grief or pain.
love and prove your per - fect will.
days and we shall wake in heaven!

Now evening comes

Stracathro 8 6 8 6 (CM)

Words: from *Te Lucis ante terminum*
(Before the ending of the day)
Michael Perry
Music: C Hutcheson (1792–1860)
arranged David Iliff

1 Now even - ing comes to close___ the day, and
2 In - to your hands, e - ter - nal Friend, we
3 In wak - ing, lift our thoughts a - bove, in
4 To Fa - ther, Son and Spi - rit — praise, all

soon___ the si - lent hours shall ban - ish___ all___ our
give___ our - selves a - gain, and to___ your watch - ful
sleep - ing, guard us still, that we___ may rise___ to
mor - tal praise be given, till sleep___ at___ last___ shall

fears___ a - way, and sleep___ re - new our powers.
care___ com - mend all those___ in grief or pain.
know___ your love and prove___ your per - fect will.
end___ our days and we___ shall wake in heaven!

166(i)   Exult, creation round God's throne

Fenny Stratford   8 8 8 8 (LM)

Words: from *Exsultet* (Easter song of praise)
Christopher Idle
Music: Paul Edwards

UNISON

1 Ex - ult, cre - a - tion round God's throne! All heaven, re -

-joice! All an - gels, sing! Sal - va - tion's trum - pet

sound a - loud for Je - sus Christ, our ris - en king.

HARMONY

2 Ex - ult, O earth, in ra - diant hope; in Christ's ma -
3 Ex - ult, all Christ - ians, one in praise with our Je -

- jes - tic splen - dour shine! The Lord is here, the
- ru - sa - lem a - bove! This roof shall ring with

vic - tory won, the dark - ness drowned in light di - vine.
Eas - ter songs that e - cho Christ's re - deem - ing love.

OPTIONAL VERSE

Exult in God, pure well of truth;
in Christ, fresh fountainhead of grace;
in Spirit, flowing stream of life –
eternal Joy our hearts embrace.

This version is compatible with the Unison setting.
Original key: A
If the piece is sung by choir alone the original key is preferable.

166(ii) **Exult, creation round God's throne**

Agincourt 8 8 8 8 (LM)

Words: from *Exsultet* (Easter song of praise)
Christopher Idle
Music: English traditional melody
arranged John Barnard

1 Ex - ult, cre - a - tion round God's throne! All
2 Ex - ult, O earth, in ra - diant hope; in
3 Ex - ult, all Christ - ians, one in praise with

heaven, re - joice! All an - gels, sing! Sal - va - tion's trum - pet
Christ's ma - jes - tic splen-dour shine! The Lord is here, the
our Je - ru - sa - lem a - bove! This roof shall ring with

sound a - loud for Je - sus Christ, our ris - en king.
vic - tory won, the dark - ness drowned in light di - vine.
Eas - ter songs that e - cho Christ's re - deem - ing love.

OPTIONAL VERSE
Exult in God, pure well of truth;
in Christ, fresh fountainhead of grace;
in Spirit, flowing stream of life –
eternal Joy our hearts embrace.

I will sing the Lord's high triumph 167(i)

Tyddyn Llwyn 8 7 8 7 8 7 7

Words: from Exodus 15, *The Easter Liturgy*
Christopher Idle
Music: E Morgan (1846–1920)

1 I will_ sing the Lord's high_ tri-umph, rul-ing earth and_ sky and
2 By the_ storm and at the_ moun-tain grace and judge-ment both are
3 Who is_ like the God of_ Is-rael, faith-ful, ho-ly,_ throned a-
4 Praise our_ God, who in his thun-der led a na-tion through the

sea; God, my_ strength, my song, my_ glo-ry, my sal-
shown; all who_ planned his peo-ple's_ ru-in power di-
-bove? Stretch-ing_ out the arm of_ an-ger, yet he
sea; praise the_ one whose blood re-leased us from our

-va-tion now is he. Through the_ wa-ters, through the_ wa-ters, God has_
-vine has_ o-ver-thrown. Na-tions trem-ble, na-tions trem-ble; God has_
guides us_ by his love. To our_ home-land, to our_ home-land, God will_
deep-er_ sla-ve-ry. Al-le-lu-ia, al-le-lu-ia, Christ is_

brought us li-ber-ty, God has brought_ us li-ber-ty.
made his mer-cy known, God has made_ his mer-cy known.
see us safe-ly move, God will see_ us safe-ly move.
ris-en: we_ are free; Christ is ris-en: we are free!

167(ii) I will sing the Lord's high triumph

Westminster Abbey 8 7 8 7 8 7

Words: from Exodus 15, *The Easter Liturgy*
Christopher Idle
Music: H Purcell (1659–1695)

1 I will sing the Lord's high triumph, rul-ing earth and
2 By the storm and at the moun-tain grace and judge-ment
3 Who is like the God of Is-rael, faith-ful, ho-ly,
4 Praise our God, who in his thun-der led a na-tion

sky and sea; God, my strength, my song, my glo-ry,
both are shown; all who planned his peo-ple's ru-in
throned a-bove? Stretch-ing out the arm of an-ger,
through the sea; praise the one whose blood re-leased us

my sal-va-tion now is he. Through the wa-ters,
power di-vine has o-ver-thrown. Na-tions trem-ble.
yet he guides us by his love. To our home-land,
from our deep-er sla-ve-ry. Al-le-lu-ia,

through the wa-ters, God has brought us li-ber-ty.
na-tions trem-ble; God has made his mer-cy known.
to our home-land, God will see us safe-ly move.
al-le-lu-ia, Christ is ris-en: we are free!

LITURGICAL
PSALMS

8L Psalm 8.1–9

O Lord, our Lord:
how great is your name in all the world!
A **Your glory fills the skies.**
B **Your praise is sung by children.**
C **You silence your enemies.**

I look at the sky your hands have made, the moon and stars you put in place:
ALL **Who are we that you care for us?**

You made us less than gods:
ALL **to crown us with glory and honour.**

You put us in charge of creation:
A **the beasts of the field.**
B **the birds of the air.**
C **the fish of the sea.**

O Lord, our Lord:
ALL **how great is your name in all the world!**

Glory to the Father, and to the Son,
and to the Holy Spirit:
as it was in the beginning, is now,
and shall be for ever. Amen.

The congregation may divide at A, B *and* C.

24L Psalm 24.1–10

The earth is the Lord's, and everything in it:
the world, and all who live here.

He founded it upon the seas:
and established it upon the waters.

E Who has the right to go up the Lord's hill;
who may enter his holy temple?
Those who have clean hands
and a pure heart,
who do not worship idols
or swear by what is false.

They receive blessing continually from the Lord:
and righteousness
from the God of their salvation.

Such are the people who seek for God:
who enter the presence of the God of Jacob.

D Fling wide the gates, open the ancient doors:
that the king of glory may come in.

E Who is the king of glory?
The Lord, strong and mighty,
the Lord mighty in battle.

D Fling wide the gates, open the ancient doors:
that the king of glory may come in.

E Who is he, this king of glory?
The Lord almighty,
he is the king of glory.

Glory to the Father, and to the Son,
and to the Holy Spirit:

as it was in the beginning, is now,
and shall be for ever. Amen.

E – *enquirer*, D – *director, or these lines may also be said by the minister.*

33L Psalm 33.1–22

Sing joyfully to the Lord, you righteous:
it is right that his people should praise him.

Praise the Lord with the harp:
A **make music to him on the strings.**

Sing to the Lord a new song:
B **play skilfully, and shout for joy.**

For the word of the Lord is right and true:
ALL **and all his work is faithfulness.**

The Lord loves righteousness and justice:
A **his endless love fills the earth.**

By the word of the Lord the skies were formed:
B **his breath created moon and stars.**

Let all the earth fear the Lord:
ALL **the people of the world revere him.**

For he spoke, and it came to be:
A **he commanded, and all was made.**

The Lord holds back the nations:
B **he thwarts their evil intent.**

God's purposes are sure:
ALL **his plans endure for ever.**

Happy is the nation whose God is the Lord:
A **happy the people he makes his own.**

The eyes of the Lord are on those who fear him:
B **who trust in his unfailing love.**

We wait in hope for the Lord:
A **he is our help and shield.**

In him our hearts rejoice:
B **we trust his holy name.**

May your constant love be with us, Lord:
ALL **as we put our hope in you. Amen.**

The congregation – and ministers – may divide at A *and* B.

36L Psalm 36.5–9

Your love, O Lord, reaches the heavens:
A **your faithfulness extends to the skies.**

Your righteousness is towering like the mountains:
B **your justice is like the great deep.**

How precious is your love, O God:
A **we find shelter beneath your wings!**

We feast on the food you provide:
B **we drink from the river of your goodness:**

For with you is the fountain of life:
ALL **in your light we see light. Amen.**

The congregation – and ministers – may divide at A *and* B.

40L(i) Psalm 40.1–3

I waited patiently for the Lord:
he turned and heard my cry.

He pulled me out of the slimy pit:
out of the mud and mire.

He set my feet upon a rock:
and made my step secure.

He put a new song in my mouth:
a hymn of praise to God.

Many will see it and fear;
and put their trust in the Lord. Amen.

40L(ii) Psalm 40.4–16

Happy are those who trust in God:
who do not worship idols.

Sacrifice and offering you do not desire:
A **but you want my ears to be open.**

So I said, 'Lord I come:
B **obedient to your word.'**

I delight to do your will, O God:
A **and keep your teaching in my heart.**

I'll tell the world your saving news:
B **you know my lips will not be sealed.**

I have not hid your righteousness:
A **but speak of all your salvation, Lord.**

I do not hide your faithful love:
B **but share your mercy with them all.**

May all who come to you be glad; may all who
know your saving power for ever say:
ALL **How great is the Lord! Amen.**

The congregation – and ministers – may divide at A *and* B.

46L Psalm 46.1–11

God is our refuge and strength:
an ever-present help in trouble.

Therefore we will not fear:
A **though the earth should shake,**
B **though the mountains fall into the sea,**
A **though the waters surge and foam,**
B **though the mountains shake and roar.**

The Lord almighty is with us:
ALL **the God of Jacob is our fortress.**

There is a river whose streams make glad the
city of God: the holy place where the Most
High dwells.
A **God is within her, she will not fall:**
B **God will help her at break of day.**

Nations are in uproar, kingdoms fall:
A **God lifts his voice –**
B **the earth melts away.**

The Lord Almighty is with us:
ALL **the God of Jacob is our fortress.**

Come and see what God has done:
ALL **his devastation on the earth!**

He stops the wars throughout the world:
A **he breaks the bow and shatters the spear –**
B **he sets the shield on fire.**

V Be still, and know that I am God: I will be
exalted over the nations, I will be exalted over
the earth.

The Lord Almighty is with us:
ALL **the God of Jacob is our fortress. Amen.**

The congregation may divide at A *and* B; V *can be a distant voice, or said by the minister.*

47L Psalm 47.1–9

Clap your hands, all you nations:
shout to God with cries of joy.

How awesome is the Lord most high:
A **the King who rules the whole wide earth!**

God has ascended to his throne:
B **with shouts of joy and sound of trumpets.**

Sing praises to our God, sing praises:
A **sing praises to our King, sing praises.**

For God is King of all the earth:
B **sing to him a psalm of praise.**

God is seated on his throne:
A **he rules the nations of the world.**

The leaders of the nations come:
B **as subjects of our holy God.**

The lords of earth belong to God:
ALL **he reigns supreme. Amen.**

The congregation may divide at A *and* B.

51L Psalm 51.6–12, and Psalm 143.6–10

O Lord, I spread my hands out to you:
A **I thirst for you like dry ground.**

Teach me to do your will, for you are my God:
B **let your good Spirit lead me in safety.**

You require sincerity and truth in me:
A **fill my mind with your wisdom.**

Create in me a pure heart, O God:
B **renew a faithful spirit in me.**

Do not cast me from your presence:
A **or take your Holy Spirit from me.**

Give me again the joy of your salvation:
B **and make me willing to obey.**

**Glory to the Father, and to the Son,
and to the Holy Spirit:
as it was in the beginning, is now,
and shall be for ever. Amen.**

The congregation may divide at A *and* B, *in which case the Gloria should be used. Psalms 51 and 143 have been grouped together to provide for an occasion when the person and work of the Holy Spirit is being considered.*

65L Psalm 65.1–13

O God, it is right for us to praise you, because you answer our prayers:

You care for the land and water it:
A **and make it rich and fertile.**

You fill the running streams with water:
B **and irrigate the land.**

You soften the ground with showers:
A **and make the young crops grow.**

You crown the year with goodness:
B **and give us a plentiful harvest.**

The pastures are filled with flocks:
A **the hillsides are clothed with joy.**

The fields are covered with grain:
ALL **they shout for joy and sing.**

**Glory to the Father, and to the Son,
and to the Holy Spirit:
as it was in the beginning, is now,
and shall be for ever. Amen.**

The congregation may divide at A *and* B.

66L Psalm 66.1–20

Praise your God with shouts of joy:
all the earth, sing praise to him.

Sing the glory of his name:
A **offer him your highest praise.**

Say to him: How great you are:
B **wonderful the things you do!**

All your enemies bow down:
C **all the earth sings praise to you.**

Come and see what God has done:
A **causing mortal men to fear –**
B **for he turned the sea to land,**
C **let his people safely through.**

We rejoice at what he does –
A **ruling through eternity,**
B **watching over all the world,**
C **keeping every rebel down.**

Praise our God, you nations, praise:
A **let the sound of praise be heard!**
B **God sustains our very lives:**
C **keeps our feet upon the way.**

Once, you tested us, O God –
A **silver purified by fire –**

Let us fall into a trap,
B **placed hard burdens on our backs –**

Sent us through the flame and flood:
C **now you bring us safely home.**

I will come to worship you:
A **bring to you my offering,**
B **give you what I said I would,**
C **when the troubles threatened me.**

All who love and honour God:
A **come and listen, while I tell**
B **what great things he did for me**
C **when I cried to him for help,**
A **when I praised him with my songs.**
B **When my heart was free from sin,**
C **then he listened to my prayer.**

Praise the Lord who heard my cry:
ALL **God has shown his love to me! Amen.**

The congregation may divide at A, B *and* C.

67L Psalm 67.1–7

May God be gracious to us and bless us:
A **and make his face to shine upon us.**

Let your ways be known upon earth:
B **your saving grace to every nation.**

Let the peoples praise you, O God:
ALL **let the peoples praise you.**

Let the nations be glad:
A **and sing aloud for joy.**

Because you judge the peoples justly:
B **and guide the nations of the earth.**

Let the peoples praise you, O God:
ALL **let all the peoples praise you.**

Then the land will yield its harvest:
A **and God, our God, will bless us.**

God will bless us:
B **and people will fear him**
ALL **to the ends of the earth. Amen.**

**Glory to the Father, and to the Son,
and to the Holy Spirit:
as it was in the beginning, is now,
and shall be for ever. Amen.**

The congregation may divide at A *and* B.

80L Psalm 80.1–19

A Hear us, O Shepherd of Israel, leader of your flock.

B Hear us from your throne above the cherubim.

C Shine forth, awaken your strength, and come to save us.
**Bring us back, O God, and save us,
make your face to shine upon us.**

A O Lord God almighty, how long will you be angry with your people's prayers?

B You have given us sorrow to eat and tears to drink.

C You have made us a source of contention to our neighbours, and our enemies insult us.
**Bring us back, O God, and save us,
make your face to shine upon us.**

A Return to us, O God Almighty, look down from heaven and see.

B Look on this vine that you planted with your own hand, this child you raised for yourself.

C Let your hand rest upon the people you have chosen, then we will not turn away from you; revive us, and we shall praise your name.
**Bring us back, O God, and save us,
make your face to shine upon us.**

**Glory to the Father, and to the Son,
and to the Holy Spirit:
as it was in the beginning, is now,
and shall be for ever. Amen.**

Ministers/leaders may divide at A, B *and* C.

93L Psalm 93.1–5

The Lord reigns, robed in majesty:
A **he arms himself with power.**

The earth is firmly set in place:
B **it never can be moved.**

Your throne was founded long ago:
A **before all time began.**

The oceans raise their voice, O Lord:
B **and lift their roaring waves.**

The Lord is mightier than the sea:
A **he rules supreme on high.**

His laws stand firm through endless days:
B **his praise for evermore.**
ALL **Amen.**

**Glory to the Father, and to the Son,
and to the Holy Spirit:
as it was in the beginning, is now,
and shall be for ever. Amen.**

The congregation may divide at A *and* B.

95L Psalm 95.1–7

M Come, let's joyfully praise our God, acclaiming the Rock of our salvation.

N Come before him with thanksgiving, and greet him with melody.

A **Our God is a great God –**
B **a king above all other gods.**

A **The depths of the earth are in his hands –**
B **the mountain peaks belong to him.**

A **The sea is his – he made it!**
B **His own hands prepared the land.**

M Come, bow down to worship him;
N kneel before the Lord who made us.

A&B **We are his people,
the sheep of his flock.**

M&N You shall know his power today –
N if you listen to his voice.

**Glory to the Father, and to the Son,
and to the Holy Spirit:
as it was in the beginning, is now,
and shall be for ever. Amen.**

The congregation may divide at A *and* B, *the ministers at* M *and* N.

96L Psalm 96.1–13

Sing to the Lord a new song:
A **sing to the Lord, all the earth.**

Sing to the Lord, praise his name:
B **proclaim his salvation each day.**

Declare his glory among the nations:
A **his marvellous deeds among the peoples.**

Great is the Lord, and worthy of praise:
B **honour him above all gods.**

Splendour and majesty surround him:
A **power and beauty fill his temple.**

Praise the Lord all people on earth:
B **praise his glory and might.**

Give him the glory due to his name:
A **bring an offering into his temple.**

Worship the Lord in his beauty and holiness:
B **tremble before him all the earth.**

Say to the nations:
ALL **The Lord is king!**

Let the heavens rejoice and the earth be glad:
A **let all creation sing for joy.**

For God shall come to judge the world:
B **and rule the people with his truth.**
ALL **Amen.**

The congregation may divide at A *and* B.

97L Psalm 97.1–12

The Lord is king:
the Lord is king!

Let the whole wide earth rejoice:
A **let the islands all be glad.**

Thunder-clouds encircle him:
B **truth and justice are his throne.**

Fire shall go before the Lord:
C **burning up his enemies.**

Lightning strikes the darkened world:
A **all the people see and fear.**

Mountains melt before our God:
B **he is Lord of all the earth.**

Skies proclaim his righteousness:
C **nations see his glory now.**

Idol-worshippers are shamed:
A **gods bow down before the Lord.**

Let Jerusalem rejoice:
B **in your faithful judgements, Lord!**

Sovereign of the universe:
C **mightier still than all the gods!**

Yet you help your saints, O Lord:
A **saving them from wicked men.**

Light will shine upon the good:
B **gladness fill the righteous heart.**

Now recall what God has done:
C **thank him,**
B **praise him,**
ALL **and rejoice!**

**Glory to the Father, and to the Son,
and to the Holy Spirit:
as it was in the beginning, is now,
and shall be for ever. Amen.**

The congregation may divide at A, B *and* C.

98L Psalm 98.1–9

Sing to the Lord a new song:
for he has done marvellous things.

His right hand and his holy arm:
have brought a great triumph to us.

A **He lets his salvation be known:**
B **his righteousness seen by the world.**
A **To us he continues his love:**
B **his glory is witnessed by all.**

Shout for joy to the Lord, all the earth:
ALL **and burst into jubilant song.**

A **Make music to God with the harp:**
B **with songs and the sound of your praise.**
A **With trumpets and blast of the horn:**
B **sing praises to God as your king.**

Let rivers and streams clap their hands:
ALL **the mountains together sing praise.**

The Lord comes to judge the whole earth:
in righteousness God rules the world. Amen.

The congregation may divide at A *and* B.

99L Psalm 99.1–9

The Lord reigns:
A **let the nations tremble!**

He sits enthroned on high:
B **let the earth shake!**

Great is the Lord our God:
ALL **exalted over all the world.**

Let the nations praise his awesome name, and say:
A **God is holy!**

Praise the Lord our God, and worship at his feet:
B **God is holy!**

Exalt the Lord our God, and worship on his holy mountain:
ALL **The Lord our God is holy!**

**Glory to the Father, and to the Son,
and to the Holy Spirit:
as it was in the beginning, is now,
and shall be for ever. Amen.**

The congregation may divide at A *and* B.

100L Psalm 100.1–5

Rejoice in the Lord, all the earth:
worship the Lord with gladness.

Remember the Lord is our God:
A **we are his flock and he made us.**

Come to his temple with praise:
B **enter his gates with thanksgiving.**

The love of the Lord will not fail:
God will be faithful for ever. Amen.

The congregation may divide at A *and* B.

103L Psalm 103.1–22

Praise the Lord, my soul:
A **all my being, praise his holy name!**

Praise the Lord, my soul:
B **and do not forget how generous he is.**

A **He forgives all my sins:**
B **and heals all my diseases.**
A **He keeps me from the grave:**
B **and blesses me with love and mercy.**

The Lord is gracious and compassionate:
A **slow to become angry,**
B **and full of constant love.**

He does not keep on rebuking:
A **he is not angry for ever.**

He does not punish us as we deserve:
B **or repay us for our wrongs.**

As far as the east is from the west:
A **so far does he remove our sins from us.**

As kind as a Father to his children:
B **so kind is the Lord to those who honour him.**

Praise the Lord, all his creation:
ALL **praise the Lord, my soul! Amen.**

The congregation may divide at A *and* B.

104L Psalm 104.1–4, 29–30

O Lord our God, you are very great:
you are clothed with splendour and majesty.

You make winds your messengers:
A **and flashes of fire your servants.**

How many are your works:
B **the earth is full of your creatures!**

When you hide your face, they are afraid:
A **when you take away their breath, they die.**

When you send your Spirit they are created:
B **and you renew the face of the earth.**

Glory to the Father, and to the Son,
and to the Holy Spirit:
as it was in the beginning, is now,
and shall be for ever. Amen.

The congregation may divide at A *and* B, *in which case the*
Gloria *should be used.*

105L Psalm 105.1–45

Give thanks to the Lord, praise his name:
A **tell the nations what he has done.**

Sing to him, sing praise to him:
B **tell of all his wonderful deeds.**

Glory in his holy name:
C **let all who worship him rejoice.**

Go to the Lord for help:
A **and worship him for ever.**

Remember the wonders he does:
B **the miracles he performs.**

He is the Lord our God:
C **he judges the whole wide earth.**

He keeps his word and covenant:
A **for a thousand generations.**

The covenant he made with Abraham:
B **the oath he swore to Israel.**

He brought them out of Egypt:
C **and none of them was lost.**

He gave a cloud for covering:
A **a pillar of fire by night.**

He gave them bread from heaven:
B **and water from the rock.**

He brought his people out rejoicing:
C **his chosen ones with shouts of joy.**

ALL **Praise the Lord!**

Glory to the Father, and to the Son,
and to the Holy Spirit:
as it was in the beginning, is now,
and shall be for ever. Amen.

The congregation – and ministers/leaders – may divide at
A, B *and* C.

107L Psalm 107.1–31

Give thanks to the Lord, for he is good:
his love endures for ever.

Repeat these words in praise to the Lord:
all those he has redeemed.

Some sailed the ocean in ships:
A **they earned their way on the seas.**

They saw what the Lord can do:
B **his wonderful deeds in the deep.**

For he spoke and stirred up a storm:
A **and lifted high the waves.**

Their ships were thrown in the air:
B **and plunged into the depths.**

Their courage melted away:
A **they reeled like drunken men.**

They came to the end of themselves:
B **and cried to the Lord in their trouble.**

He brought them out of distress:
A **and stilled the raging storm.**

They were glad because of the calm:
B **he brought them safely to harbour.**

Let them give thanks to the Lord:
ALL **for his unfailing love.**

Glory to the Father, and to the Son,
and to the Holy Spirit:
as it was in the beginning, is now,
and shall be for ever. Amen.

The congregation may divide at A *and* B.

111L <small>Psalm 111.1–10</small>

Praise the Lord:
praise the Lord!

With my whole heart I will thank the Lord: in the company of his people. Great are the works of the Lord:
^A **those who wonder, seek them.**

Glorious and majestic are his deeds:
^B **his goodness lasts for ever.**

He reminds us of his works of grace:
^A **he is merciful and kind.**

He sustains those who fear him:
^B **he keeps his covenant always.**

All he does is right and just:
^A **all his words are faithful.**

They will last for ever and ever:
^B **and be kept in faith and truth.**

He provided redemption for his people, and made an eternal covenant with them:
<small>ALL</small> **holy and awesome is his name!**

The fear of the Lord is the beginning of wisdom; he gives understanding to those who obey:
<small>ALL</small> **to God belongs eternal praise!**

Glory to the Father, and to the Son, and to the Holy Spirit: as it was in the beginning, is now, and shall be for ever. Amen.

The congregation may divide at A *and* B.

113L <small>Psalm 113.1–9</small>

^A Praise the Lord:
praise the Lord!

^B You servants of the Lord, praise his name:
let the name of the Lord be praised, both now and for evermore!

^A From the rising of the sun to the place where it sets:
the name of the Lord be praised!

^B The Lord is exalted above the earth:
his glory over the heavens.

^A Who is like the Lord our God?
He is throned in the heights above –

^B Yet he bends down:
yet he stoops to look at our world.

^A He raises the poor from the dust:
and lifts the needy from their sorrow.

^B He honours the childless wife in her home:
he makes her happy, the mother of children.

<small>BOTH</small> Praise the Lord:
Amen.

The ministers/leaders may divide at A *and* B.

116L <small>Psalm 116.1–19</small>

I love the Lord because he heard my voice:
^A **the Lord in mercy listened to my prayers.**

Because the Lord has turned his ear to me:
^B **I'll call on him as long as I shall live.**

The cords of death entangled me around:
^C **the horrors of the grave came over me.**

But then I called upon the Lord my God:
^A **I said to him: 'O Lord, I beg you, save!'**

The Lord our God is merciful and good:
^B **the Lord protects the simple-hearted ones.**

The Lord saved me from death and stopped my tears:
^C **he saved me from defeat and picked me up.**

And so I walk before him all my days:
^A **and live to love and praise his holy name.**

What shall I give the Lord for all his grace?
^B **I'll take his saving cup, and pay my vows.**

Within the congregation of his saints:
^C **I'll offer him my sacrifice of praise.**

Praise the Lord:
<small>ALL</small> **Amen, amen!**

The congregation may divide at A, B *and* C.

117L <small>Psalm 117.1–2</small>

Praise the Lord, all you nations:
^A **praise him, all you people!**

Great is his love towards us:
^B **his faithfulness shall last for ever.**

Praise the Lord:
Amen.

The congregation may divide at A *and* B.

118L <small>Psalm 118.1–29</small>

^M Give thanks to the Lord, for he is good:
his love endures for ever.

^M All those who fear the Lord shall say:
His love endures for ever.

^W Open for me the gates of the Temple; I will go in and give thanks to the Lord.

^M This is the gate of the Lord, only the righteous can come in.

^W I will give thanks because you heard me; you have become my salvation.

^C The stone which the builders rejected as worthless turned out to be the most important of all:
<small>ALL</small> **The Lord has done this – what a wonderful sight it is!**

W This is the day of the Lord's victory – let us be happy, let us celebrate:
ALL **O Lord save us – O Lord, grant us success.**

M May God bless the one who comes in the name of the Lord:
ALL **The Lord is God – he has been good to us!**

C From the Temple of the Lord, we bless you.

D With branches in your hands, start the procession and march round the altar:

W You are my God and I will give you thanks:
ALL **You are my God, and I will exalt you.**

M Give thanks to the Lord, for he is good:
His love endures for ever. Amen.

M – *minister,* W – *worshipper – from doorway, then moving through congregation,* C – *choir/chorus,* D – *director – in matter-of-fact tone.*

122L Psalm 122.1–8

I was glad when they said to me:
let us go to the house of the Lord!

Pray for the peace of Jerusalem:
A **may those who love our land be blessed.**

May there be peace in your homes:
B **and safety for our families.**

For the sake of those we love we say:
ALL **Let there be peace! Amen.**

**Glory to the Father, and to the Son,
and to the Holy Spirit:
as it was in the beginning, is now,
and shall be for ever. Amen.**

The congregation may divide at A – *male voices, and* B – *female voices.*

124L Psalm 124.1–8

If the Lord had not been on our side – now let Israel say:
If the Lord had not been on our side –
A **when enemies attacked us,**
B **when their anger flared against us,**
C **they would have swallowed us alive.**
A **The flood would have engulfed us,**
B **the torrent would have swept over us,**
C **the waters would have drowned us.**

Praise the Lord:
A **who has not given us up to their teeth.**
B **We have escaped like a bird from the snare:**
C **the snare is broken and we are free.**

Our help is in the name of the Lord:
ALL **who made heaven and earth. Amen.**

The congregation may divide at A, B *and* C.

126L Psalm 126.1–6

When the Lord brought us back from slavery:
A **we were like those who dream.**

Our mouths were filled with laughter:
B **our tongues with songs of joy.**

Then those around us said, 'The Lord has done great things for them':
A **The Lord has done great things for us,
and we are filled with joy.**

Those who sow in tears
B **shall reap with songs of joy.**

**Glory to the Father, and to the Son,
and to the Holy Spirit:
as it was in the beginning, is now,
and shall be for ever. Amen.**

The congregation may divide at A *and* B, *in which case the* Gloria *should be used.*

128L Psalm 128.1–6

The pilgrims' song:
A **Blessed are those who fear the Lord,**
B **who walk in his ways.**

You will eat the fruit of your work; blessings and prosperity will be yours:
A **Blessed are those who fear the Lord,**
B **who walk in his ways.**

Your wife will be like a fruitful vine within your house; your children will be like young olive trees around your table:
A **Blessed are those who fear the Lord,**
B **who walk in his ways.**

May the Lord bless you all the days of your life; may you have prosperity; may you live to see your children's children:
ALL **Peace be with you. Amen.**

The congregation may divide at A *and* B.

134L Psalm 134.1–3

You servants of the Lord,
who stand in his temple at night:
A **praise the Lord!**

Lift your hands in prayer to the Lord:
B **in his sanctuary, praise the Lord!**

May the Lord who made the heaven and earth bless you from Zion:
ALL **Amen!**

**Glory to the Father, and to the Son,
and to the Holy Spirit:
as it was in the beginning, is now,
and shall be for ever. Amen.**

The congregation may divide at A *and* B, *in which case the* Gloria *should be used.*

136L Psalm 136.1–26

A Give thanks to God, for he is good:
A **his love shall last for ever!**

B Give thanks to him, the God of gods:
B **his love shall last for ever!**

C Give thanks to him, the Lord of lords:
C **his love shall last for ever!**

A For God alone works miracles:
A **his love shall last for ever!**

B The skies were made at his command:
B **his love shall last for ever!**

C He spread the seas upon the earth:
C **his love shall last for ever!**

A He made the stars to shine at night:
A **his love shall last for ever!**

B He made the sun to shine by day:
B **his love shall last for ever!**

C He brought us out from slavery:
C **his love shall last for ever!**

A He leads us onward by his grace:
A **his love shall last for ever!**

B He saves us from our enemies:
B **his love shall last for ever!**

C Give thanks to God, for he is good:
C **his love shall last for ever!**
ALL **Amen!**

The congregation must divide at A, B *and* C *saying the whole stanza, OR both ministers and congregation should divide.*

143L Psalm 143.6–10, and Psalm 51.6–12

O Lord, I spread my hands out to you:
A **I thirst for you like dry ground.**

Teach me to do your will, for you are my God:
B **let your good Spirit lead me in safety.**

You require sincerity and truth in me:
A **fill my mind with your wisdom.**

Create in me a pure heart, O God:
B **and renew a faithful spirit in me.**

Do not cast me from your presence:
A **or take your Holy Spirit from me.**

Give me again the joy of your salvation:
B **and make me willing to obey.**

**Glory to the Father, and to the Son,
and to the Holy Spirit:
as it was in the beginning, is now,
and shall be for ever. Amen.**

The congregation may divide at A *and* B, *in which case the Gloria should be used. Psalms 143 and 51 have been grouped together to provide for an occasion when the person and work of the Holy Spirit is being considered.*

147L Psalm 147.1–20

O praise the Lord, sing out to God:
such praise is right and good.

The Lord restores Jerusalem:
A **he brings the exiles home.**

He heals all those with broken hearts:
B **he bandages their wounds.**

He counts the number of the stars:
C **he calls them each by name.**

How great and mighty is the Lord:
A **immeasurably wise!**

He raises up the humble ones:
B **and brings the mighty down.**

Sing hymns of triumph to his name:
C **make music to our God!**

He spreads the clouds across the sky:
A **he showers the earth with rain.**

He sends the animals their food:
B **he feeds the hungry birds.**

His true delight is not the strong:
C **but those who trust his love.**

Extol the Lord, Jerusalem:
A **let Zion worship God!**

For God shall keep your people safe:
B **and bring your harvest home.**

He gives commandment to the earth:
C **his will is quickly done.**

He spreads like wool the falling snow:
A **how cold the frosty air!**

He sends the wind, the warming rain:
B **and melts the ice away.**

His laws he gives to Israel:
C **and Judah hears his word.**

He does not favour other lands:
ALL **so, praise the Lord. Amen!**

The congregation may divide at A, B *and* C.

148L Psalm 148.1–14

Praise the Lord!

Praise the Lord from the heavens:
praise him in the heights above.

Praise him, all his angels:
A **praise him, all his heavenly host.**

Praise him, sun and moon:
B **praise him, all you shining stars.**

Let them praise the name of the Lord:
ALL **Praise the Lord!**

Praise the Lord from the earth:
A **praise him, great sea creatures.**

Praise him, storms and clouds:
B **praise him, mountains and hills.**

Praise him, fields and woods:
A **praise him, animals and birds.**

Praise him, rulers and nations:
B **praise him, old and young.**

Let them praise the name of the Lord:
ALL **Praise the Lord! Amen.**

The congregation may divide at A *and* B.

149L Psalm 149.1–9

Praise the Lord:
praise the Lord!

Sing a new song to the Lord:
A **let the people shout his name!**

Praise your maker, Israel:
B **hail your king, Jerusalem.**

Sing and dance to honour him:
A **praise him with the strings and drums.**

God takes pleasure in his saints:
B **crowns the meek with victory.**

Rise, you saints, in triumph now:
A **sing the joyful night away!**

Shout aloud and praise your God!
B **Hold aloft the two-edged sword!**

Let the judgement now begin:
A **kings shall fall and tyrants die.**

Through his people, by his word:
B **God shall have the victory!**

Praise the Lord:
ALL **praise the Lord!**

**Glory to the Father, and to the Son,
and to the Holy Spirit:
as it was in the beginning, is now,
and shall be for ever. Amen.**

The congregation – and ministers – may divide at A
and B.

150L 150.1–6

Praise the Lord!

Praise God in his sanctuary:
praise his strength beyond the skies!

Praise him for his acts of power:
A **praise him for his surpassing greatness.**

Praise him with the sounding of the trumpet:
B **praise him with the harp and lyre.**

Praise him with tambourine and dancing:
A **praise him with the strings and flute.**

Praise him with the clash of cymbals:
B **praise him with resounding cymbals.**

Let everything that has breath praise the
Lord:
ALL **Praise the Lord! Amen.**

**Glory to the Father, and to the Son,
and to the Holy Spirit:
as it was in the beginning, is now,
and shall be for ever. Amen.**

The congregation may divide at A *and* B.

Legal Information, Notes and Acknowledgements

Psalms and Liturgical Texts

Those seeking to reprint material in this book which is the property of Jubilate Hymns or associated authors (attributed '/Jubilate Hymns') may write to The Copyright Secretary, Jubilate Hymns Ltd, 61 Chessel Avenue, Southampton SO2 4DY. In the United States of America these copyrights and those of Timothy Dudley-Smith, Peter Cutts, Fred Kaan and Fred Pratt Green are administered by Hope Publishing Company, Carol Stream, Illinois 60188. Addresses of other copyright-holders can also be supplied.

Jubilate Hymns, Marshall Pickering Communications, Scripture Union, Thankyou Music, Word (UK) Ltd – along with other copyright-holders whose titles they administer (Celebration Services, Maranatha!, Word & Music etc.) have uniform concessions and rates. Details are available from the Copyright Secretary, Jubilate Hymns Ltd.

Most of these publishers also combine to offer a licensing scheme for limited term reproduction. Where this is felt to be an advantage, application should be made to the Christian Music Association at Glyndley Manor, Stone Cross, Pevensey, East Sussex BN24 5BS (0323 440440). Hymns copyrighted Stainer & Bell may not be reprinted or photocopied under any blanket licensing scheme, but should be cleared individually with Stainer & Bell Limited.

Liturgical (Responsive) Psalms

These texts are the copyright of the Editor, and are available for local reproduction subject to acknowledgement of source in the form 'Reprinted from *Psalms for Today* with the permission of Jubilate Hymns Ltd' (or, in the USA, '. . . of Hope Publishing Company, Carol Stream, Illinois 60188').

Recording and Broadcasting

Jubilate Hymns and associated authors, and Word & Music are members of the Mechanical Copyright Protection and Performing Right Societies.

The Alternative Service Book

The Alternative Service Book 1980 (ASB) is © the Central Board of Finance of the Church of England 1980.

The content of Holy Communion Rite A and Morning or Evening Worship is drawn from alternative services authorised for use in the Church of England. The complete alternative services of Holy Communion Rite A, Morning Prayer and Evening Prayer may be found in ASB. These services are authorised for use in the Church of England pursuant to Canon B2 of the Canons of the Church of England until 31st December 2000. The copyright in ASB and in individual alternative services is held by the Central Board of Finance of the Church of England and they may not be reproduced without permission.

The text of the Apostles' Creed, as printed in Morning Prayer and Evening Prayer, is copyright © 1970, 1971, 1975 International Consultation on English Texts (ICET). The Lord's Prayer in its modern form is adapted from the ICET version.

Acknowledgements

We owe our thanks most particularly to those authors and composers who readily created or adapted their work to meet the need for fluent and congregational texts and music settings of quality and relative simplicity. We mention especially those to whom we turned time and again for help and support: John Barnard, Timothy Dudley-Smith, Christopher Idle, Brian Foley, David Mowbray, Norman Warren and Paul Wigmore.

For application of her special expertise to the text of the liturgical (responsive) psalms we thank Rev. Kathleen Bowe of Cliff College.

For the major task of copyright clearance and assistance in preparing the work for publication we thank Bunty Grundy, Ann Darlington and Sylvia Bleasdale of Jubilate Hymns. For their encouragement and professionalism we acknowledge the contribution of publishers and typesetters – especially Hodder and Stoughton's Tim Anderson, Dick Douglas and Kathy Dyke, and Barnes' Michael Mack Smith.

Michael Perry (Editor)
David Iliff (Music Editor)

Themes Index to the Psalms and Canticles

Italics indicate the numbers of canticles and other liturgical hymns

absolution – 24B

acknowledge God – 100D

actions (ours; see also: 'behaviour', 'deeds') – 61A, 139B

acts (of God; see also: 'deeds', 'wonders') – 145B, 150B, 150C

adoration – 19A, 31A, 145A, 146

advent – 16A, 24A, 24B, 28, 44, 50A, 50B, 73, 81, 85A, 96L, 97, 98A, 98B, 98C, 98L, 122B, 132, *156A, 158A, 158B*

Advent services (and Sundays before Christmas; see also: 'advent') – 28, 46A, 46B, 46L, 50A, 50B, 75, 85, 96A, 96L, 97, 97L, 98A, 98B, 98C, 98L, *156A, 158A, 158B, 158C, 160A, 160B, 160C*

adversary (see also: 'enemies', 'oppressor') – 143A

advice – 1C

age (old) – 71A, *162A, 162B, 162C*

ages (see also: 'generations') – 145A, 146

aggression – 43B

aggressors – 76

agony (see also: 'pain') – 22A

All Saints-tide services (see also: 'Saints days') – 1C, 15A, 15B, 33L, 97, 97L, 145A, 145B, 149L, *156A, 156B, 156C, 164B, 164C*

all-seeing (God; see also: 'seeing') – 73

altar – 43A, 84C, 118L

angels – 73, 78, 91A, 103A, 103B, 148A, 148C, 148L, *154A, 154B, 154C, 156B, 156C, 166*

anger (God's) – 30A, 37A, 38, 60, 63B, 80L, 85, 88, 95A, 95C, 103C

anger (God is slow to anger) – 103B

animals – 8A, 8C, 147L, 148A, 148L

anniversary (see also: 'dedication/consecration . . .' etc) – 48A

Annunciation – 113, 113L, 131A, 131B, *160A, 160B, 160C*

anointing – 23A, 23C

anointing (Christ's) – 45

answer to prayer (see also: 'prayer') – 3A, 20A, 22A, 34B, 38, 61B, 65B, 65L, 66A, 91A, 116A, 143A

anthems – 96A, 148B

anxiety – 16A, 55, 127B

anxiety (about the future) – 69A

anxiety (worldly) – 84A

apostles – *156A, 156C, 156D*

approach to God – 24B

approval (God's) – 127A

arm (God's) – 28, 98A, 98C, 98L, 123B, *160A, 160B, 160C, 167*

ascension – 47B, 68A, 93A, 99L, 110, 113L, *152B, 157A, 157B*

Ascensiontide services (see also: 'ascension') – 8C, 21, 24B, 45, 47B, 47L, 68A, 93A, 93B, 93L, 99L, *156B, 156C, 156D, 157A, 157B, 159A, 163A, 163B, 163C, 164A, 164B, 164C*

Ash Wednesday (see also: 'lent services') – 6, 51A, 51B, 90A, 90B

assurance (see also: 'confidence') – 19B, 20A

atheism (see also: 'unbelief') – 1A, 10, 14

atheist – 53, 137

atonement (Jesus') – 116A

autumn – 84C, 148C

awaking – 5

away from home (see also: 'exile') – 61A

babies – 8A, 8C, 107

Baptism (service of thanksgiving for) – 116A, 116B, 116L, *167*

battle – 43A

beasts (see also: 'animals', 'creatures') – 8B, 148A, 148B, 148C

beauty (of God and creation) – 8B, 29A, 52, 90B, 104A

behaviour (see also: 'living') – 19A, 19C, 50A

Bible reading (see: 'receiving . . .')

Bible Sunday – 1A, 1B, 1C, 12B, 19A, 19B, 19C, 62A, 95B, 119A, 119B, 119C

birds – 8A, 8C, 8L, 11, 84A, 84C, 147L, 148A, 148B, 148C, 148L, *154A, 154B*

bitterness – 10

blamelessness (see also: 'innocence') – 15A, 26, 119C

blessing – 1A, 1C, 3A, 14, 20A, 23B, 24C, 24L, 39, 67A, 67C, 67L, 69A, 84A, 84C, 103L, 106A, 107, 112, 115, 123B, 125, 128A, 128B, 128L, 133A, 133B, 134A, 134B, 134C, 134L

blindness (see also: 'light') – 81, 82

blood (see: 'cross', 'ransom', 'redemption')

boasting (see also: 'pride') – 52, 73, 75, 128B

bounty (God's; see also: 'generosity') – 146

bow – 46B, 46L

brass (instruments; see also: 'trumpet') – 149A, 150A

bread – 105L, 146

breath (God's) – 104L

breeze (see also: 'wind') – 147B

bribery – 15B

broken-hearted, the – 51B, 147B, 147L

brokenness (see also: 'contrition', 'penitence', 'repentance') – 51B

brother – 122B

building – 127A, 127B

burdens – 54, 66L, 122A

busy (being busy) – 121B, 121C, 121D, 127B

call, calling – 78, 132

calm – 107L, 121B, 131A

captivity – 126A

care for people (see: 'help', 'kindness')

care (God cares for us) – 8A, 38, 61A, 91A, 103A, 104B, 116A, 121B, 122A

care, lack of (in the world) – 130A

care (negative sense; see also: 'anxiety', 'worry') – 55

cattle – 107, 148A, 148B

cedar – 80, 87, 92A

celebration (see: 'joy', 'praise', 'worship')

changelessness of God – 93A, 93B, 100A, 100B, 103A

changing seasons – 148C

cheer – 31A

359

Liturgical Index to the Psalms and Canticles

Italicised subjects refer to the Themes Index

Advent (and Sundays before Christmas; see also: *'advent'*) – 28, 46A, 46B, 46L, 50A, 50B, 75, 85, 96A, 96L, 97, 97L, 98A, 98B, 98C, 98L, 122B, 132, 153A, 153B, 153C, 156A, 158A, 158B, 158C, 160A, 160B, 160C

All Saints-tide (see also: 'Saints Days') – 1C, 15A, 15B, 33L, 97, 97L, 145A, 145B, 149L, 156A, 156B, 156C, 164B, 164C

Anniversary (see: 'dedication/consecration')

Annunciation Festival – 113A, 113L, 131A, 131B, 160A, 160B, 160C

Ascensiontide (see also: *'ascension'*) – 8C, 21, 45, 47A, 47B, 47L, 68A, 93A, 93B, 93L, 99L, 155A, 155B, 155C, 156A, 156B, 156C, 157A, 157B, 159A, 163A, 163B, 163C, 163D, 164A, 164B, 164C

Ash Wednesday (see also: 'Lent') – 6, 51A, 51B, 90A, 90B

Baptism (service of thanksgiving for; see also: *'baptism'*) – 116A, 116B, 116L, 167

Bible Sunday – 1A, 1B, 1C, 12B, 19A, 19B, 19C, 62A, 95B, 119A, 119B, 119C

Christmas Day, Sundays after Christmas – 98B, 98L, 102A, 160A, 160B, 160C, 163A, 163B, 163C, 163D

church anniversary (see: 'dedication/consecration')

civic/national occasions – 9, 15B, 44, 60, 67A, 67B, 67C, 67L, 72, 78, 82, 85, 96A, 96L, 100A, 100B, 100C, 100D, 100L, 111A, 111L, 117A, 117B, 117L, 149A

commissioning/ordination – 37A, 47A

Communion (see: 'Holy Communion')

Creation Sunday – 8A, 8B, 8C, 8L, 19A, 19B, 19C, 29A, 100B, 100C, 104A, 104B, 104L, 136A, 136L, 147L, 148A, 148B, 148C, 148L, 151, 154A, 154B, 154C, 159B (evening), 164B, 164C

dedication/consecration (anniversary) of a church – 15A, 24B, 24C, 24L, 48A, 84A, 84C, 89A, 100B, 100L, 118A, 118L, 122A, 122B, 122L, 127A, 127B, 132, 147B, 149A, 149L, 150B, 150C, 150L, 161B

Easter Day, Sundays after Easter – 8A, 18A, 18B, 105L, 113L, 114, 118A, 118L, 152A, 152B, 166, 167

Education Sunday – 1A, 1B, 8A, 8B, 8L, 40L, 104A, 111L, 119A, 119B, 119C, 143L

Epiphany – 110, 153A, 162A, 162B, 162C, 162D

evening worship – 36, 36L, 43A, 63A, 63B, 121B, 121C, 121D, 134A, 134B, 134C, 134L, 141, 159A, 159B, 159C, 165A, 165B

funeral services – 23A, 23B, 23C, 31A, 39, 42A, 42B, 49B, 71A, 84B, 90A, 90B, 103A, 103B, 103C, 103L, 121A, 121B, 121C, 130A, 130B, 130C, 139A, 139B, 162A, 162B, 162C

Good Friday (see also: *'passiontide'*) – 13A, 22A, 69A, 158A, 158B, 158C, 163A, 163B, 163C, 163D

Harvest Festival (see also: *'harvest'*) – 65A, 65B, 65L, 67A, 67B, 67C, 67L, 104A, 104B, 126B, 126C, 126L, 145A, 145B, 147A, 147B, 147L, 148A, 148B, 148C, 148L

healing services – 103B, 103L, 147A, 147B, 147L, 165B

Holy Communion (Thanksgiving for; see also: *'communion'*) – 23B, 34A, 116L, 157A, 157B

Lent (and Sundays before Easter) – 10, 11, 13A, 14, 17, 19A, 19B, 26, 27A, 31A, 32A, 38, 40A, 40L, 42A, 42B, 51A, 51B, 54, 61A, 61B, 69A, 70, 84A, 86A, 91A, 103C, 103L, 122A, 122B, 122L, 125, 126A, 130B, 130C, 139A, 139B

marriage services – 67B, 121B, 121D, 127B, 128A, 128B, 128L

missionary occasions (see also: *'proclaiming'*, *'witness'*) – 46A, 46B, 46L, 47A, 47L, 67A, 67B, 67L, 87, 96A, 96B, 96L, 97, 98B, 98L, 100B, 100C, 100L, 117A, 117B, 117L, 138A, 157A, 164C

morning worship – 5, 16A, 19B

Mothering Sunday – 67B, 100L, 112, 113L, 121B, 122L, 127A, 127B, 128A, 128B, 128L, 131A, 131B, 160A, 160B, 160C

New Year services – 47A, 67C, 67L, 102A

Palm Sunday – 8L, 22A, 24A, 24B, 24C, 24L, 45, 69A, 163A, 163B, 163C, 163D

Passiontide – 13A, 22A, 158A, 158B, 158C, 163A, 163B, 163C, 163D

Pentecost (see also: *'Spirit'*) – 51L, 104L, 143A, 143L

Remembrance services (see also: 'civic/national occasions', *'remembrance'*) – 44, 46A, 46B, 47A, 47L, 93, 93L, 111A, 111L, 124A, 124L, 126B, 126C, 126L, 130A, 130B, 130C, 137A

Rogation-tide (see also: *'rogation'*) – 65A, 65L, 67B, 67C, 67L, 107, 126B, 126C, 126L, 147L

Saints' days – 32A, 34A, 34B, 112, 156A, 156B, 156C, 164B, 164C

Sea Sunday – 57A, 93B, 93L, 107, 107L, 151

social responsibility services – 9, 12A, 72, 76, 82, 87, 99A, 113L, 130A, 146, 160A, 160B, 160C

Thanksgiving for the birth of a child – 20A, 116B, 116L

Thanksgiving services – 89A, 136L, 145A, 145B, 147A, 147B, 147L, 148B, 148L, 149A, 149L, 150A, 150B, 150L, 154A, 155B, 155C

Transfiguration (see also: *'face of God'*) – 84A

Trinity Sunday – 93, 93L, 97, 97L, 99L, 149A, 155A, 156A, 156B, 156C, 156D, 157A, 157B, 161A, 161B, 164A, 164B, 164C; evening: 159A, 159B, 159C, 165A, 165B

unity services – 122A, 122B, 122L, 133A, 133B

371

Morning and Evening Prayer Index to the Canticles

MORNING CANTICLES

Venite (Psalm 95.1–7, Psalm 98.9)
Come with all joy to sing to God – 95A
Come worship God who is worthy of honour – 95B
O come, let us sing out to the Lord (ASB) – 95C,
151
Come, let's joyfully praise our God (LIT) – 95L

Jubilate (Psalm 100)
Come, rejoice before your maker – 100A
Sing, all creation – 100B
O shout to the Lord in triumph
all the earth (ASB) – 100C
With joyful shouts acclaim the Lord – 100D
Rejoice in the Lord, all the earth (LIT) – 100L

The Easter Anthems (1 Corinthians 5.7–8;
Romans 6.9–11; 1 Corinthians 15.20–22)
Now lives the Lamb of God – 152A
Christ our passover
has been sacrificed for us (ASB) – 152B

FIRST LESSON

Benedictus (The Song of Zechariah – Luke 1.68–
79)
O bless the God of Israel – 153A
O praise our great and faithful God – 153B
Blessed be the Lord the God of Israel (ASB) – 153C

A Song of Creation/Benedicite (The Song of the

Three Children 35–64 – The Greek Old
Testament)
Bless the Lord, created things – 154A
Angels, praise him – 154B
Bless the Lord, all created things (ASB) – 154C

Great and wonderful (Revelation 15.3–4)
Great and wonderful your deeds – 155A
Wonderful your deeds, Lord – 155B
Great and wonderful are your deeds (ASB) – 155C

SECOND LESSON

Te Deum (A Christian hymn from the fourth
century)
God of gods, we sound his praises – 156A
God, we praise you! God, we bless you – 156B
You are God and we praise you (ASB) – 156C
Great is the Lord we now acclaim – 156D

Gloria in excelsis (A Christian hymn from the
fourth century – based on Luke 2.14)
All glory be to God on high – 157A
Glory to God in the highest (ASB) – 157B

Saviour of the world (A free church hymn from
the nineteenth century)
Saviour Christ, in mercy come – 158A
Jesus, saviour of the world – 158B
Saviour of the world (ASB) – 158C

EVENING CANTICLES

Psalm 134
Bless the Lord as day departs – 134A
Come, praise the Lord, all you his servants – 134B
Come bless the Lord all you servants of the Lord
(ASB) – 134C
You servants of the Lord (LIT) – 134L

O gladsome light (A Christian hymn from the
third century)
Light of gladness, Lord of glory – 159A
Light of gladness, shining radiance – 159B
O gladdening light, O grace (ASB, adapted) – 159C

The Easter Anthems (1 Corinthians 5.7–8;
Romans 6.9–11; 1 Corinthians 15.20–22)
Now lives the Lamb of God – 152A
Christ our passover has been sacrificed for us (ASB)
– 152B

FIRST LESSON

Magnificat (The Song of Mary – Luke 1.46–55)
My soul proclaims
the greatness of the Lord – 160A
With Mary let my soul rejoice – 160B

My soul proclaims
the greatness of the Lord (ASB) – 160C

Cantate Domino (Psalm 98)
Sing to God new songs of worship – 98A
Sing a new song to the Lord – 98B
O sing to the Lord a new song (ASB) – 98C
Sing to the Lord a new song (LIT) – 98L

Bless the Lord (The Song of the Three Children
29–32 – The Greek Old Testament)
Bless the Lord, our fathers' God – 161A
Bless the Lord the God of our fathers – 161B
Bless the Lord the God of our fathers (ASB) – 161C

SECOND LESSON

Nunc dimittis
(The Song of Simeon – Luke 2.29–32)
Faithful vigil ended – 162A
Lord, now let your servant go his way in peace –
162B
Lord now let your servant go in peace (ASB) – 162C
Now at last your servant
can depart in peace – 162D

Deus misereatur (Psalm 67)
Mercy, blessing, favour, grace – 67A
May God be gracious, may we see his face – 67B
May God be gracious to us and bless us (ASB) – 67C
May God be gracious to us and bless us (LIT) – 67L

The Song of Christ's glory (Philippians 2.6–11)
All praise to Christ – 163A
Before the heaven and earth – 163B
Christ Jesus was in the form of God (ASB) – 163C
Though Christ put on our frail humanity – 163D

Glory and honour
  (Revelation 4.11; 5,9,10,12,13)
Heavenly hosts in ceaseless worship – 164A
Glory and honour – 164B
Glory and honour and power (ASB) – 164C

Saviour of the world (A free church hymn from
  the nineteenth century)
Saviour Christ, in mercy come – 158A
Jesus, saviour of the world – 158B
Saviour of the world (ASB) – 158C

OTHER LITURGICAL HYMNS

Before the ending of the day (From a Latin hymn
  of before the eighth century)
Before the ending of the day – 165A
Now evening comes to close the day – 165B

Exsultet (Song of praise
  from the Western Easter liturgy)
Exult, creation round God's throne – 166

Exodus 15 (Song of praise
  from the Western Easter liturgy)
I will sing the Lord's high triumph – 167

Lectionary Index to the Psalms and Canticles

Italics indicate Lectionary appointed psalms; italicised words indicate references to the Themes Index

9 before Christmas (The Creation) – 8A, 8B, 8C, 8L, 19A, 19B, 19C, *29A*, 100B, 100C, *104A, 104B, 104L*, 136A, 136L, 147L, *148A, 148B, 148C, 148L, 150A, 150B, 150C, 150L*, 151, 154A, 154B, 154C, 159B (evening), 164B, 164C

8 before Christmas (The Fall) – 5, 10, 14, 15A, 19A, 19B, 19C, *25A*, 36, 38, 51A, 51B, 52, 78, 84B, 103A, 103B, 103C, 103L, 106A, 116A, 119C, 124A, *130B, 130C, 139A, 139B*

7 before Christmas (The Election of God's People: Abraham) – *1A, 1B, 1C*, 4A, *32A*, 34A, *36A, 36L*, 50B, 67B, 80, 80L, 89A, 98A, 98B, 100A, 100B, 100C, 100D, 102A, 103C, 103L, *105L*, 111L, *136A, 136L*

6 before Christmas (The Promise of Redemption: Moses) – 10, 12A, 65A, *66A, 66L*, 67A, 68A, 77, 78, 81, 84A, 85, 87, 93B, 95A, 95B, 105L, *106A*, 107, 114, 136A, 167

5 before Christmas (The Remnant of Israel) – 1B, 37A, 39, 40A, 42A, 42B, 50B, 61B, 62A, 66A, 71A, *75, 76, 80, 80L*, 99A, 116B, *147A, 147B, 147L*, 153A, 153B, 153C, 156A, 156C, 156D, 158A, 158B

Advent 1 (The Advent Hope) – *18A, 18B*, 28, 46A, 46B, 46L, *50A, 50B, 68A*, 75, *82*, 85, 96A, 96L, 97, 97L, 98A, 98B, 98C, 98L, 132, 153A, 153B, 153C, 156A, 158A, 158B, 158C, 160A, 160B, 160C

Advent 2 (The Word of God in the Old Testament) – 1A, 1B, 1C, 12A, *19A, 19B, 19C*, 49A, 49B, 50B, 62A, 95B, *119A, 119B, 119C*

Advent 3 (The Forerunner) – *11, 14*, 46A, 46B, 46L, 47A, 47L, *80, 80L*, 96A, 96B, 96L, 97, 98B, 98L, *126A, 126B, 126C, 126L*, 153A, 153B, 153C, 157A, 164C

Advent 4 (The Annunciation) – *40A, 40L(i), 40L(ii)*, 45, *113A, 113L, 123A, 123B, 131A, 131B, 160A, 160B, 160C*

Christmas 1 (The Incarnation) – 47A, 67C, 67L, *84A, 84B, 84C*, 98B, 98L, 102A, *116A, 116B, 116L*, 122A, 122B, 122L, *132*, 160A, 160B, 160C, 163A, 163B, 163C, 163D

Christmas 2 (The Holy Family) – *27A*, 67B, *85, 87, 89A*, 100L, 112, 113B, 121B, 122L, 127A, 127B, 128A, 128B, 128L, 131A, 131B, 160A, 160B, 160C, *162A, 162B, 162C, 162D*

Epiphany 1 (Revelation: The Baptism of Jesus) – *29A, 30A, 36A, 36L, 46A, 46B, 46L*, 47A, *47B, 47L, 89A*, 110, 116A, 116B, 116L, 117A, 117B, 117L, 153A, 155A, 162A, 162B, 162C, 162D

Epiphany 2 (Revelation: The First Disciples) – 4A, *15A, 15B, 16A*, 34B, 78, 80, 80L, 95B, 96A, 98B, *100A, 100B, 100C, 100D, 100L*, 111A, *121A, 121B, 121C, 121D, 126A, 126B, 126C, 126L*, 127A, 132, 138A, *145A, 145B*, 155B, 155C

Epiphany 3 (Revelation: Signs of Glory) – 8L, 19A, 19B, 19C, 29A, *33A, 33L*, 46A, *46B, 46L*, 50B, 81, 85, 93B, 96B, 97L, 102A, 104B, *107, 107L*, 108A,

113A, 113L, 115, 131A, *136, 136L*, 145A, 145B, 156A, 156C

Epiphany 4 (Revelation: The New Temple) – 15A, 24B, 24C, 24L, *34A, 34B, 48A, 50A, 50B, 84A, 84C*, 100B, 100L, 118A, 118L, 122A, 122B, 122L, 127A, 127B, 147B, 149A, 149L, 150B, 150C, 150L, 161B

Epiphany 5 (Revelation: The Wisdom of God) – 19A, 19B, 19C, 32A, *36A, 36L, 49A, 49B*, 50A, 51A, 68A, 81, 82, *92A*, 104A, 111L, *119A, 119B, 119C, 119L*, 138A, 143L, 147A

Epiphany 6 (Revelation: Parables) – *25A, 43A, 43B*, 75, 76, *127A, 127B, 128A, 128B, 128L, 133A, 133B*

9 before Easter (Christ the Teacher) – 1A, 1B, 8A, 8B, 8L, *34A, 34B*, 40L, *71A*, 73, *103A, 103B, 103C, 103L*, 104A, 111L, 119A, 119B, 119C, 143L

8 before Easter (Christ the Healer) – 103B, 103L, *131A, 131B, 137A, 139A, 139B*, 142A, 146, *147A, 147B, 147L*, 165B

7 before Easter (Christ, the Friend of Sinners) – 8A, 25A, *32A, 56A, 57A*, 68A, *103A, 103B, 103C, 103L, 119A, 119B, 119C, 119L, 122B*

Lent 1 (The King and the Kingdom: Temptation) – 10, 11, 13A, 14, 17, 19A, 19B, 26, 27A, 31A, 32A, 38, 40A, 40L(i), 40L(ii), 42A, 42B, *51A, 51B*, 54, 61A, 61B, 69A, 70, 84A, 86A, 90A, 90B, *91A*, 103C, 103L, *119A, 119B, 119C, 119L*, 122A, 122B, 122L, 125, 126A, *130B, 130C, 139A, 139B*, 142A

Lent 2 (The King and the Kingdom: Conflict) – 1A, 5, *18A, 18B*, 19A, 20A, 26, 27A, 43B, 56A, 63A, *119C*, 130A, 141

Lent 3 (The King and the Kingdom: Suffering) – *31A*, 39, 40L(i), 40L(ii), 46A, 46B, 47A, 50A, 51B, 84A, 90B, 104L, *115*, 116L, *119A, 119B, 119C, 119L*, 127A, 139B, 141 (see also: *'prayer'*)

Lent 4 (The King and the Kingdom: Transfiguration) – 11, 13A, *18A, 18B, 23A, 23B, 23C*, 24C, 27, 44, 51A, 61B, 63A, 67A, 67B, 67C, 67L, 80L, 84A, 84B, 90A, 104L, *119A, 119B, 119C*, 143A, 151, 159B, 159C

Lent 5 (The King and the Kingdom: The Victory of the Cross) – 19B, *22A*, 34B, 49B, 52, *66A*, 73, 76, 103B, 107L, 111L, 119A, 126A, *130B*, 142A, *143A, 143L*, 153A, 153C, 156A, 156B, 156C, 156D, 158B, 158C, 163A, 163B, 163C, 164A, 164B, 164C (see also: *'freedom', 'liberty', 'release'*)

Palm Sunday (The Way of the Cross) – 8A, 8B, 8C, 8L, 13A, 19B, *22A, 24A, 24B*, 24C, 24L, *45, 61A, 61B, 62A, 62B, 69A*, 100B, 158A, 158B, 158C, 163A, 163B, 163C, 163D

Easter – *18A, 18B*, 105L, *113L, 114, 117A, 117B, 117L, 118A, 118L*, 152A, 152B, *156A, 156B, 156C, 156D*, 166, 167

Easter 1 (The Upper Room / The Bread of Life) – Year 1: 18A, *30A, 34A, 34B*, 42A, 42B, *48A*, 49B, *115, 145A, 145B*, 152A, 166, 167. Year 2: *30A*,

Alphabetical Index to Tunes

First Lines Index to the Psalms and Canticles

Italics indicate titles of canticles and liturgical hymns

The Order for Holy Communion Rite A

from The Alternative Service Book 1980

The Prayers of the Congregation

THE PREPARATION

The Lord be with you
and also with you.

Almighty God,
to whom all hearts are open,
all desires known,
and from whom no secrets are hidden:
cleanse the thoughts of our hearts
by the inspiration of your Holy Spirit,
that we may perfectly love you,
and worthily magnify your holy name;
through Christ our Lord.   Amen.

There is no other commandment greater than
these.
Amen. Lord, have mercy.

Almighty God, our heavenly Father,
we have sinned against you
**   and against our fellow men,**
in thought and word and deed,
through negligence, through weakness,
through our own deliberate fault.
We are truly sorry,
and repent of all our sins.
For the sake of your Son Jesus Christ,
**   who died for us,**
forgive us all that is past;
and grant that we may serve you
**   in newness of life**
to the glory of your name.   Amen.

Or

Almighty God, our heavenly Father,
we have sinned against you,
through our own fault,
in thought and word and deed,
and in what we have left undone.
For your Son our Lord Jesus Christ's sake,
forgive us all that is past;
and grant that we may serve you
**   in newness of life**
to the glory of your name.   Amen.

Lord, have mercy.   Christ, have mercy.
Lord, have mercy.   **Christ, have mercy.**

            Lord, have mercy.
            Lord, have mercy.

Glory to God in the highest,
and peace to his people on earth.

Lord God, heavenly King,
almighty God and Father,
we worship you, we give you thanks,
we praise you for your glory.

Lord Jesus Christ,
**   only Son of the Father,**
Lord God, Lamb of God,
you take away the sin of the world:
have mercy on us;
you are seated at the right hand of the Father:
receive our prayer.

For you alone are the Holy One,
you alone are the Lord,
you alone are the Most High,
Jesus Christ,
with the Holy Spirit,
in the glory of God the Father.   Amen.

THE MINISTRY OF THE WORD

This is the word of the Lord.
Thanks be to God.

Glory to Christ our Saviour.

This is the Gospel of Christ.
Praise to Christ our Lord.

We believe in one God,
the Father, the almighty,
maker of heaven and earth,
of all that is,
seen and unseen.

We believe in one Lord, Jesus Christ,
the only Son of God,
eternally begotten of the Father,
God from God, Light from Light,
true God from true God,
begotten, not made,
of one Being with the Father.
Through him all things were made.
For us and for our salvation
he came down from heaven;
by the power of the Holy Spirit
he became incarnate of the Virgin Mary,
**   and was made man.**
For our sake he was crucified
**   under Pontius Pilate;**
he suffered death and was buried.
On the third day he rose again
in accordance with the Scriptures;
he ascended into heaven
and is seated at the right hand of the Father
He will come again in glory
to judge the living and the dead,
and his kingdom will have no end.

We believe in the Holy Spirit,
the Lord, the giver of life,
who proceeds from the Father and the Son.
With the Father and the Son
   he is worshipped and glorified.
He has spoken through the Prophets.

We believe in one holy catholic
   and apostolic Church.
We acknowledge one baptism
   for the forgiveness of sins.
We look for the resurrection of the dead,
and the life of the world to come.   Amen.

Lord, in your mercy
hear our prayer.

Merciful Father,
accept these prayers
for the sake of your Son,
our Saviour Jesus Christ.   Amen.

We do not presume
to come to this your table, merciful Lord,
trusting in our own righteousness,
but in your manifold and great mercies.
We are not worthy
so much as to gather up the crumbs
   under your table.
But you are the same Lord
whose nature is always to have mercy.
Grant us therefore, gracious Lord,
so to eat the flesh of your dear son Jesus Christ
and to drink his blood,
that we may evermore dwell in him
and he in us.   Amen.

Or

Most merciful Lord,
your love compels us to come in.
Our hands were unclean,
our hearts were unprepared;
we were not fit
even to eat the crumbs
   from under your table.
But you, Lord,
are the God of our salvation,
and share your bread with sinners.
So cleanse and feed us
with the precious body and blood of your Son,
that he may live in us and we in him;
and that we, with the whole company of Christ,
may sit and eat in your kingdom. Amen.

THE MINISTRY OF THE SACRAMENT

The peace of the Lord be always with you
and also with you.

Yours, Lord, is the greatness, the power,
the glory, the splendour, and the majesty;
for everything in heaven and on earth is yours.
All things come from you,
and of your own do we give you.

The Lord is here.
His Spirit is with us.

Lift up your hearts.
We lift them to the Lord.

Let us give thanks to the Lord our God.
It is right to give him thanks and praise.

We proclaim your great and glorious name,
for ever praising you and saying:
Holy, holy, holy Lord,
God of power and might,
heaven and earth are full of your glory.
Hosanna in the highest.

Blessed is he who comes
   in the name of the Lord.
Hosanna in the highest.

Do this, as often as you drink it,
in remembrance of me.
Christ has died:
Christ is risen:
Christ will come again.

[We worship you, Father almighty,
in songs of everlasting praise:
Blessing and honour and glory and power
be yours for ever and ever.]
Amen.

As our Saviour taught us, so we pray.
Our Father in heaven,
hallowed be your name,
your kingdom come,
your will be done,
on earth as in heaven.
Give us today our daily bread.
Forgive us our sins
as we forgive those who sin against us.
Lead us not into temptation
but deliver us from evil.
For the kingdom, the power,
   and the glory are yours
now and for ever.   Amen.

We break this bread
to share in the body of Christ.
Though we are many, we are one body,
because we all share in one bread.

AFTER COMMUNION

Father of all,
we give you thanks and praise,
that when we were still far off
you met us in your Son
    and brought us home.
Dying and living,
he declared your love,
gave us grace,
and opened the gate of glory.
May we who share Christ's body
live his risen life;
we who drink his cup
bring life to others;
we whom the Spirit lights
give light to the world.
Keep us firm
in the hope you have set before us,
so we and all your children
    shall be free,
and the whole earth
live to praise your name;
through Christ our Lord.   **Amen.**

Almighty God,
we thank you for feeding us
with the body and blood of your Son
    Jesus Christ
Through him we offer you our souls and bodies
to be a living sacrifice.
Send us out
in the power of your Spirit
to live and work
to your praise and glory.   **Amen.**

Go in peace to love and serve the Lord.
In the name of Christ.   Amen.

Or

Go in the peace of Christ.
Thanks be to God.

Morning or Evening Worship
drawn from The Alternative Service Book 1980

INTRODUCTION
We have come together
    as the family of God
in our Father's presence
to offer him praise and thanksgiving,
to hear and receive his holy word,
to bring before him
    the needs of the world,
to ask his forgiveness of our sins,
and to seek his grace,
that through his Son Jesus Christ
we may give ourselves to his service.

SENTENCE
If we say we have no sin,
we deceive ourselves,
and the truth is not in us.
If we confess our sins,
God is faithful and just,
and will forgive us our sins,
and cleanse us
    from all unrighteousness.

CONFESSION
Let us confess our sins to almighty God:

Almighty God, our heavenly Father,
we have sinned against you
    and against our fellow men,
in thought and word and deed,
through negligence,
    through weakness,
through our own deliberate fault.
We are truly sorry
and repent of all our sins.
For the sake of your Son Jesus Christ,
    who died for us,
forgive us all that is past;
and grant that we may serve you
    in newness of life
to the glory of your name.   Amen.

Or

Almighty God, our heavenly Father,
we have sinned against you,
through our own fault,
in thought and word and deed,
and in what we have left undone.
For your Son our Lord Jesus Christ's sake,
forgive us all that is past;
and grant that we may serve you
    in newness of life
to the glory of your name.   Amen.

ABSOLUTION
Almighty God, who forgives all who truly repent,
have mercy upon *you*, pardon and deliver *you* from
all *your* sins, confirm and strengthen *you* in all goodness, and keep *you* in life eternal; through Jesus
Christ our Lord.   Amen.

LITANY
O Lord, open our lips:
and our mouth shall proclaim your praise.

Let us worship the Lord:
all praise to his name.

Glory to the Father, and to the Son,
and to the Holy Spirit:
as it was in the beginning, is now,
and shall be for ever.   Amen.

RESPONSES TO READINGS
This is the word of the Lord:
thanks be to God.

THE APOSTLES' CREED
I believe in God, the Father almighty,
creator of heaven and earth.
I believe in Jesus Christ, his only Son, our Lord.
He was conceived
    by the power of the Holy Spirit
and born of the Virgin Mary.
He suffered under Pontius Pilate,
was crucified, died, and was buried.
He descended to the dead.
On the third day he rose again.
He ascended into heaven,
and is seated at the right hand of the Father.
He will come again
    to judge the living and the dead.
I believe in the Holy Spirit,
the holy catholic Church,
the communion of saints,
the forgiveness of sins,
the resurrection of the body,
and the life everlasting.   Amen.

Lord, have mercy upon us.
Christ, have mercy upon us.
Lord, have mercy upon us.

THE LORD'S PRAYER
Our Father in heaven,
hallowed be your name,
your kingdom come,
your will be done,
on earth as in heaven.
Give us today our daily bread.
Forgive us our sins
as we forgive those
    who sin against us.
Lead us not into temptation
but deliver us from evil.
For the kingdom, the power, and the glory
    are yours
now and for ever.   Amen.

RESPONSES

Show us your mercy, O Lord;
and grant us your salvation.

O Lord, save the Queen;
and teach her counsellors wisdom.

Let your priests be clothed with righteousness;
and let your servants shout for joy.

O Lord, make your ways known upon the earth;
let all nations acknowledge your saving power.

Give your people the blessing of peace;
and let your glory be over all the world.

Make our hearts clean, O God;
and renew a right spirit within us.

MORNING COLLECTS

Almighty and everlasting Father,
we thank you
that you have brought us safely
to the beginning of this day.
Keep us from falling into sin
or running into danger;
order us in all our doings;
and guide us to do always
what is right in your eyes;
through Jesus Christ our Lord.   **Amen.**

Or

Eternal God and Father,
you create us by your power
and redeem us by your love:
guide and strengthen us by your Spirit,
that we may give ourselves in love and service
to one another and to you;
through Jesus Christ our Lord.   **Amen.**

EVENING COLLECT

Lighten our darkness,
Lord, we pray;
and in your mercy defend us
from all perils and dangers of this night;
for the love of your only Son,
our Saviour Jesus Christ.   **Amen.**